VETERAN & VINTAGE TRANSIT

a guide to North America's mass transit museums, tourist trolley operators and private mass transit vehicle collections compiled by

Andrew D. Young

Published 1997

Archway Publishing
P.O. Box 410903
St. Louis, MO 63141-0903

First published 1997

Archway Publishing St. Louis
P.O. Box 410903 St. Louis, MO 63141-0903

© 1997 Andrew D. Young

ISBN 0-9647279-2-7

Library of Congress Catalog Card 97-071783

Production, design and cover art by QB Printing & Graphics, St. Louis, MO
All photos by Andrew D. Young

Front Cover Photo:
Yakima Electric Railway Museum ex-Porto car 1776 crosses the Naches River on its way from Selah to Yakima in September 1989.

Rear Cover Photos:
Top: Former Porto car 204 is one of several that have been beautifully restored for service in Memphis. The car is northbound and about to enter Main Street Mall on October 24, 1993.

Bottom: Lowell National Historical Park replica open car 1602 leaves Boott Mill for the Visitors' Center on May 31, 1994.

Introduction and Acknowledgments

This book lists North America's main collections of preserved mass transit vehicles. It is not exhaustive or complete in every detail, but an overview in the shape of a convenient pocket guide. Listings are alphabetical by country (Canada, U.S.), by province or state, then city or town. Information comes from many sources, including personal observation over twenty-five years. However, as not even the vehicles' owners necessarily know the provenance, pedigree or even the full identity of a given artifact, errors may exist. Entries are corrected (as far as possible) to January 1, 1997. For future editions, the author welcomes updates, additions and corrections.

Entries are broken down into six categories.

1. ***City and suburban cars.*** Horse, cable or electric streetcars for city or suburban service.

2. ***Interurban cars.*** Cars for high-speed electric passenger, express package or freight service between small towns and a large city or cities.

3. ***Rapid transit cars.*** Cars for elevated or subway lines.

4. ***Work cars and locomotives.*** Cars for maintenance-of-way work, train haulage and freight services on city, suburban, interurban, elevated or subway lines.

5. ***Electric trolley buses.***

6. ***Motor buses.***

Vehicles are listed numerically, based on the paint scheme and lettering they currently exhibit. Previous or subsequent incarnations are listed in parentheses. For example:

CAR	BUILDER & DATE	TRUCKS	CAR TYPE
Illinois Terminal 101	American, 1917	St. Louis 61A	DE DT Center-entrance suburban

(Originally Alton, Granite & St. Louis 61, then St. Louis & Alton 61.)

Numbers expressed as 49 (I), 4601 (II), or 152 (III) mean that these were the first, second or third vehicles of this operating entity to bear the same number.

Unless otherwise stated, all collections are open to the public. Most have an operational street railway or electric interurban component, many are purely city tourist trolley operations, some include subway, rapid transit, buses and electric trolley buses as part of their display, a few are purely rapid transit or bus museums.

Information on opening and operation is general; change is constant. Always check with the institution before making a long trip specifically for the purpose. Don't forget to ask if any special events are coming up. Lots of equipment normally tucked away out of sight makes special runs at such times.

Some mass transit collections are part of a larger railroad museum, but railroad artifacts are not listed. Most museums can supply an exhibit inventory that includes railroad artifacts, if they have them, for a few dollars. Pure railroad museums and tourist railroad operations are not covered in this guide. An explanation of abbreviations and a glossary is provided at the end of the guide.

My thanks are due to the hard-working volunteer administrative staff of all the collections listed, who took time out to answer many arcane questions and to Scott Becker and Paul Hammond of the Association of Railway Museums, Tom Konieczny of Belleville, IL., Richard Kunz of Chicago, IL., Dr. Art Martin and Bradley Martin of Fort Smith AR., Donald T. Curry, D. B. Minnich and Jim Schantz of Kennebunkport ME., Paul Averdung of Milwaukee, WI., Cliff Perry of Olmsted Falls OH., Steve Morgan of Portland OR., Jeffrey Moreau of Sacramento CA., Mark Goldfeder, Willis Goldschmidt and Don Scott of St. Louis, MO., John McKane of San Rafael, CA, Joshua Shields of Seattle WA., Nick Kallas of Union, IL., Mac Sebree of Vancouver WA., Russell E. Schultz of Wauwatosa WI. and Edward Metka of Windber PA. Also to Ian M. Dougill, Dr. Michael Harrison and A. Keith Terry of Leeds, England and to John H. Price of Peterborough, England who for more than thirty-five years kept the world abreast of international developments through his monthly Museum News and Heritage columns in the British magazine Light Rail and Modern Tramway.

Riverfront line, New Orleans. Former Melbourne car 452 approaches the Toulouse Street Station on February 12, 1993, with the Mississippi River in the background. With the regauging of the line in 1997, the Melbourne cars were sold to Memphis Main Street Trolley.

Forward

Human beings are never satisfied. No sooner has one generation made a technological or social advance of any kind than the next gets all misty-eyed with nostalgia and moves heaven and earth to go back again. Look around you. The evidence is everywhere, from the "retro" look of today's cameras to the resurrection of the vinyl LP. And if they can't go back again, you can bet they'll want to set up a museum to memorialize the status quo ante.

Nowhere is this phenomenon more marked than in mass transit. An essential public utility, most folk give it as much thought as they do water, electrical or sewage systems, that is to say, none at all unless there's a breakdown, in which case all hell breaks loose. But when it's gone, there's always been folk prepared to do something about it. In the trolley's heyday nearly a century ago, it was stagecoaches and covered wagons that were preserved. When the bus was supreme, the trolley was the apple of the collector's eye. With mass transit now emphasizing light and heavy rail, the bus in its turn is becoming a sought-after museum piece.

Though North America's first mass transit museum was established in 1939, it wasn't until well after World War II that the museum movement began to flourish, just at the time when private transit (the automobile) gained its ascendancy. Between 1950 and 1975, mass transit in general and the electric trolley in particular seemed doomed to extinction and most transit museums of the period were dedicated almost exclusively to trolley preservation.

The same period saw steam disappear from the railroads and passenger train service shrink to regionally-operated commuter lines centered on the major cities and Amtrak's few national routes. Many tourist railroads began at this time, but few dedicated rail museums. So in this era, many trolley museums saw themselves as museums of rail rather than mass transit and acquired heavy railroad equipment along with streetcars or interurbans. Some now have phenomenal railroad collections and are as dedicated to operating steam and diesel trains as they are streetcars.

Other than for the private collectors, whose interests are eclectic or commercial, two very different groups collect mass transit exhibits today: those creating or building museums and those running tourist services. Museums are mainly devoted to the streetcar. Bus, ETB, subway and rapid transit exhibits are collected to supplement the streetcar collection, although some now focus on these areas, especially motor buses. The tourist service people are exclusively street railway oriented.

The Mass Transit Museum

Museums entertain, educate and inform the public about mass transit, particularly the electric street railway, which dominated city streets from 1890 until 1940. All are 501 (c) 3 not-for-profit corporations that collect, conserve, preserve, restore, maintain and demonstrate their exhibits, together with the ancillary hardware that sustained them. They also preserve the paper and photographic records of their subject and interpret what they have. They are there for the long haul. They are building for the generations. Most date from the 1940s and 1950s when the streetcar's extinction seemed imminent. Set up by cash-poor amateurs, sweat equity was the name of the game. They have achieved a level of sophistication in fundraising, conservation, restoration, intepretation and presentation undreamed of forty years ago, but self-help and sweat equity remain dominant in mass transit museum "corporate" culture.

For the visitor used to the slickness of the average theme park, that's a breath of fresh air. There's an amiable "Ma and Pa Kettle" quality in even the best museums that's comfortingly down-home friendly in an old-fashioned way. These are not well-packaged tourist traps stocked with cardboard people wearing plastic smiles but home-spun places with real human beings from every walk of life going about their business of restoring and demonstrating yesterday's mass transit for the public of today.

Enjoy the show. You won't be disappointed. Ride the cars, enjoy the summer breeze, savor the sights, smells and sounds of vintage machinery, learn something from the conductor's end-of-the-line talk, wander through any barn or shop not specifically closed to the public (few are), taking care to stand behind any protective rope or fence.

You'll thrill at the sight of cars in every state of repair, from decayed chicken coop to factory-fresh sparkle. You'll marvel at the tools, equipment and working conditions reminiscent of fifty (and more) years ago that bring those cars back from the dead. You'll be astonished at the multitude of skills needed just to keep a ninety-year old car in working order, skills kept alive only by the dedication of museum personnel, mostly unpaid volunteers.

That's not all museums do. Behind the scenes, they collect and maintain libraries, archives, photographs, movies, drawings, anything you care to know about mass transit in general and local street railways in particular. Just set up an appointment in advance if you want to do anything other than browse.

All museums share a mission to inform, educate and entertain the public on mass transit and its effect on city life. But you can't visualise the enormity of that impact in the absence of the urban landscape and those who populate it. Mass transit was (and remains) a product of the crowded city street, not the four-houses-to-an-acre tract of the post-war suburbs and certainly not the prairie or the forest primeval, no matter how many cities could boast at least one such line. The green-fields site of the typical museum is at odds with the popular perception and the actual history of mass transit. City cars and buses (though not interurbans) so proudly displayed, are fish out of water.

Moreover, back in the city, they were not the stars of the show, as they undoubtedly are at the museums, but bit players in a bigger and more profoundly significant drama: urban life, how we lived it and how our attitudes to it changed. They came into being not as tangible manifestations of some abstract intellectual exercise in applied technology, but as practical responses to pressing and specific needs of urban life.

But as the riding public's needs changed, as first the private transit companies and then the quasi-public or wholly public agencies that replaced them proved to be fiscal sinkholes, as cities and urban areas changed along with the way they were used and perceived, so car and bus design was altered in an ever-more-desperate effort to keep up.

One can only comprehend the otherwise minor and unmimportant differences in vehicle types that museums typically emphasize by understanding that historical truth. Recreating the urban environment is the most visitor-friendly way to do it. Traditionally, few green-fields museums could afford to.

The Tourist Trolley

The coming of the tourist trolley addressed this particular weakness. In tourist operations, the city streetcar is closer to its historical role as bit player in the urban drama. Generally located in (and an integral part of) reviving downtown or midtown areas retaining much of the former density of occupation and activity, there is an authentic feel to tourist lines unmatched by the green-fields museums.

So what exactly are they? Richard Kunz, editor of <u>The New Electric Railway Journal</u> defines a tourist trolley as satisfying at least three of the four following criteria:

- Possessing genuine historic or facsimile electric rail equipment operating in a setting recalling the area's own electric railway heritage.

- Running on rails and operating electrically.

- Conducting its operations independently of any established trolley museum or transit operator in or close to the heart of an urban area.

- Providing services directed primarily towards tourists or other non-regular riders.

The tourist trolley made its North American debut in the 1970s and blossomed in the 1980s. The folks attracted to starting and sustaining such ventures were as much pioneers as the sweat equity museum people of the previous generation. Indeed they have directly benefitted from their predecessors' experience and frequently attract museum stalwarts to join them. But they differ from the earlier museum pioneers in three fundamental ways.

First, their love for the trolley is not the core of their interest, but part of a larger concern for conserving and preserving the neighborhood, the environment and the community of which they are a part. It is rooted in civic or commercial imperatives rather than the educational mission of the museums

Second, without exception, they are organically connected with their neighborhoods and communities in a way few museums have ever been.

Third, from the outset, tourist trolley folks are fiscally, socially and politically savvy. Sweat equity has no place in their corporate culture. They maximise the possibility of success by being well-organized from the get-go, lining up backing from a representative cross-section of a community: not just John Q. Public or the dedicated trolley buff but also the neighborhood movers and shakers who can rattle cages at City Hall, pry money loose from grantmakers and corral corporate largess for the larger public good.

Vintage Light Rail

Vintage light rail uses historic cars to provide transit services grafted onto downtown sections of new light rail lines, added as a stand-alone component to existing systems or on a line that has had the dumb luck to have survived intact from an earlier age.

It seems to work. Unlike the museums, or even the tourist trolleys, people daily ride vintage light rail in their thousands. One can argue that such installations blur the line between the museum (with its demonstration rides) and real-life mass transit so effectively that vintage light rail may well prove to be the next trend in mass transit. Vintage light rail services don't cover their costs from the farebox but they bring tangible, quantifiable benefits to the areas they serve, well beyond the narrow vision of an individual project's fiscal bottom line.

That's the greatest strength of vintage light rail and tourist trolleys. They, even more than the museums, are living, breathing urban time warps, deliberately created to turn back the clock and so making a major contribution to improving the quality of life in their urban neighborhood. A secondary benefit comes from acting as a bridge to atttract back people who've abandoned both the city and mass transit.

Their existence has made the traditional trolley museum conceptually obsolete. The museums of the 1940s and 1950s wanted to recreate a world they believed was doomed to extinction. They were only partially successful. They had the vehicles, but not the urban environment. The tourist trolleys and vintage light rail have not recreated that world either, but they haven't had to. They have instead taken the cars back to their proper urban environment, initially without regard to long-term survival (now being addressed) and collection depth (which is not) that the museums believed were essential to their own mission.

So if the museums' mission is no longer relevant to today's circumstances, will they re-define their role? If they intend to survive, they'd better. This is no longer a world where mass transit is on the way to extinction. New light rail systems (modern trolleys) open every year, tourist trolleys proliferate, vintage light rail is common and more people have resumed the riding habit.

The Shock of the Old

While people regard mass transit generally as a necessary evil, they like trolleys, especially old trolleys. But why? What is it in the human psyche that responds to the sight of an eighty-year old trolley car going about its business? What is it about the 1990s that makes people keen to while away a pleasant few hours in some gigantic urban history theme park and persuades civic and corporate leaders that there just may be some economic benefit to the local community in having them do so?

It is the seemingly out-of-joint times in which we live.

Just consider. In the last twenty years, entire TV channels have been created, devoted to reruns of 1950s and 1960s shows. Newer shows and movies recreate (sometimes at great expense) and celebrate the past – *Happy Days* or *The Waltons* on television, *American Graffiti, Back to the Future, Radio Days* or *Avalon* in the movies. Theme parks like Disneyland or Universal Studios cover an immense acreage with streets and buildings replicating the past. Fifties diners are all the rage. The public loves it all.

Behind this trend is the widely-held notion that not so very long ago, life was civil, decent, humane and manageable, that life is no longer so and that we've lost, not gained, as a result. Today's preoccupation with recreating middle-class urban neighborhoods, the (inaccurate) perception of the 1950s as a golden age of social and political tranquility, is part of that mind-set, the driving force behind the post-World War II phenomenon of folk, industrial and urban museums.

The mass transit museums, the tourist trolleys, the many civic and and historic neighborhood revival projects across the continent, are fueled by this sense of loss, this sense that we are not now what we once were, that our best years as a civilized community are past, that the old certainties (right or wrong) were more nourishing to the soul than the new. From this has come the notion that if we no longer live like that now, let's at least preserve something of what's left or replicate it, to remind ourselves of what we once were and maybe could be again. And that's what every project listed in this guide is all about.

A heavily-laden Waterloo, Cedar Falls and Northern 381 picks its way through the campers and RVs whose occupants are attending the 1996 Midwest Old Threshers Reunion at Mt. Pleasant, Iowa.

Seashore Trolley Museum. Lightweight Milwaukee city car 861 waits for departure time at the impressive museum Visitor Center on July 25, 1988.

The Illinois Railway Museum's Central Avenue, with Chicago electric trolley bus 9631 passing Chicago bus 3407 in September, 1988.

TABLE OF CONTENTS

DORMANT OR RECENTLY DEFUNCT
COLLECTIONS AND OPERATIONS

For its first fifty years, the St. Louis Museum of Transportation's streetcar exhibits were purely static, but in 1996 the first few hundred yards of track was electrified. Philadelphia SEPTA PCC 2740 is seen on a test run at the museum on April 20, 1997.

CANADA

Calgary

1. **Heritage Park Historical Village,** *1900 Heritage Drive SW, Calgary, AB T2V 2X3. (403) 259-1900. Standard-gauge tourist trolley and horsecar. Open daily last two weeks of May to first weekend of September, weekends to first weekend of October.*

   Heritage Park sits on a 60-acre city-owned peninsula of a man-made lake. Authentic Calgary buildings, shops and homes have been re-erected on streets themed around a specific era and staffed by costumed interpreters. The streetcar line runs from the parking lot to the main entrance and opened in the 1970s. A horse car line and steam passenger train operate inside the park.

CAR	BUILDER AND DATE	TRUCKS	CAR TYPE
Winnipeg Street Ry. Co. 8	Unknown, 1972	Pedestal	DE ST Replica horse car
Calgary Tramways 14, 15	Ottawa, circa 1914	Brill 27-E-1	DE DT City
(Double-end replicas, built by Heritage Park with parts from the originals which survived until the early 1970s.)			

2. **Calgary Transit,** *PO Box 2100, Station M, Calgary AB T2P 2M5. (403) 277-9711. CT, operating light rail and bus services in the area, owns the following vehicles. They are not publicly displayed.*

BUS	BUILDER AND DATE	SERIAL NUMBER
Calgary TS 379	CCF/Brill CD 52, 1959	17808 (Gasoline)
Calgary TS 422	CCF/Brill T44, 1947	5160 (ETB)

Edmonton

1. **Edmonton Radial Railway Society,** *PO Box 45040, Landsdowne, Edmonton AB T6H 5Y1. (403) 428-2992. Standard-gauge trolley museum in Fort Edmonton Park at Whitemud Freeway and Fox Drive. Open daily last two weeks of May to first weekend of September, Sundays in September to first Sunday of October.*

   The ERRS was formed in 1979 to formalize the running of preserved Edmonton car 1 over the High Level Bridge (last used by trolleys in 1951) for three days as a 75th birthday present to the city. A home was found in Fort Edmonton, an open-air park featuring historic Edmonton buildings, farms, shops and industries, re-erected (and staffed by costumed interpreters) as living history exhibits. The trolley links the park's several historic eras and provides internal transport, supplemented by a steam railroad on a different route. Edmonton's first-generation trolleys ceased in 1951, before the trolley museum movement took off at full bore. Nevertheless, enough bodies survived that a prime ERRS goal to rescue and restore at least one of each Edmonton car type has largely been achieved.

A. City and Suburban Cars

CAR	BUILDER AND DATE	TRUCKS	CAR TYPE
Edmonton TS 1	Ottawa, 1908	Brill 27-G	SE DT City
Brandon (ON) 6	Niles, 1913	Brill 21-E	DE ST City
Edmonton TS 13	Ottawa, 1911	Brill 27-G	SE DT City
(This car was owned by the Alberta Pioneer Railway Association between 1973 and 1981.)			
Toronto Suburban Ry. 24	Preston, 1913	Taylor	DE ST City
(Car probably built 1893, builder and owner unknown. By 1913 it was Toronto Suburban 24, with body and underframe rebuilt by Preston. Became Canadian National 15702 at Fort William (ON) hump yard and grain terminal in 1924. Car almost identical to Edmonton 7, the city's only single-truck car. Leased by the ERRS from the Canadian Railway Museum at Delson, Quebec.)			
Edmonton TS 33, 38, 42	St. Louis, 1912	St. Louis 47B (replicas built by museum)	DE DT City
Regina MUNI 42	CCF, 1928	Brill 77-E	SE DT City
(This car was for many years stored in the city of Regina by the Saskatchewan RR Historical Association.)			

A. City and Suburban Cars, *continued*

Edmonton TS 52, 53   Preston, 1913   Standard 0-50   SE DT City
(Car 52's trucks were recently traded to the Nelson Street Railway for PCC car parts.)
Calgary Tramways 60   Ottawa, 1913   Brill 27-G   SE DT City
Edmonton TS 65, 73   Preston, 1913   Standard 0-50   SE DT City
Edmonton TS 80   Ottawa, 1930   Melbourne Type 1   SE DT Lightweight city
Saskatoon MUNI 202   Cincinnati, 1918   Taylor   SE DT "Peter Witt" city
(Built for Rochester NY, entered service in Cleveland OH, sold in 1923 to London [ON] Street Railway and to Saskatoon in 1941. Retired 1951 to Western Development Museum, Moose Jaw, Saskatchewan, to Fort Edmonton 1996.)
Osaka (Japan) 247   Umebachi/Sharyo, 1921   Brill 77-E   DE DT City
(Hankai Tramway of Nankai Electric Ry., Osaka. Car rebuilt in 1947.)
Hannover (Germany) 601   Siemens-Duewag, 1970   Duewag   DE 3-truck Articulated city
Toronto TTC 4349, 4367   St. Louis/CCF, 1947   Clark B-2   SE DT Type A-6 PCC
(4349 acquired from Toronto in 1982 by Midwestern Rail Association, Winnipeg, to ERRS in 1995.)
Toronto TTC 4612   St. Louis/CCF, 1951   Clark B-2   SE DT Type A-15 PCC
(Originally Toronto Type A-8 PCC 4543.)

The body of Edmonton TS 31 (Preston, 1911, SE DT city car), the only survivor of its class, is in poor condition and is being kept to provide a pattern from which a replica can be built.

B. Work Cars and Locomotives

Toronto TTC S-40   Unknown   Unknown   Unknown
(This car was for many years at Halton County Radial Railway, Rockwood ON.)
Saskatoon MUNI 200   Ottawa, circa 1907   Ottawa single truck   DE ST Snow Sweeper/Line car
(Retired to Western Development Museum Moose Jaw, Saskatchewan in 1951, to Ft. Edmonton in 1986)

2. Edmonton Radial Railway Society, *(Strathcona trolley) PO Box 45040, Landsdowne, Edmonton AB T6H 5Y1. (403) 428-2992. Proposed standard-gauge tourist trolley.*

In 1991, Edmonton approved an ERRS proposal to run heritage cars over the High Level bridge between the Grandin light rail station and 104th Street at 85th Avenue in Strathcona, on former Canadian Pacific RR tracks linking Strathcona Station with Edmonton's Canadian National station. The 1913 bridge's top deck has a central CP railroad track, which until 1951 was flanked on either side by a trolley track. CP freight trains ran until 1994, when the Alberta Provincial government took over, giving trackage rights to the city. The city in turn revived their 1991 agreement with the ERRS to run a heritage service. In 1995, the Edmonton "Fringe" Festival (held in old Strathcona) asked the ERRS to run a trolley service between 104th and 108th Street to link two sites. Hankai 247 (with generator in tow) did the honors between August 14 and September, 1995. In 1996, the line was wired and successful test runs were made in October. When the High Level bridge remodelling is finished in 1997, the Strathcona trolley will cross into Edmonton (as envisaged back in 1991), using the bridge's original street railway poles, which have survived since 1951, to support the overhead wires. Hankai 247 will again be used, possibly joined by Edmonton 33, whose restoration as a double-end car is nearly complete. This line is physically separated from the Fort Edmonton line by several miles.

3. Edmonton Transit System, *Century Place, 9803 102A Avenue, Edmonton AB T5J 3R5. (403) 428-4145. ETS, operating light rail, bus and ETB services in the area, owns the following vehicles. They are not publicly displayed.*

A. Work Cars and Locomotives

CAR	BUILDER AND DATE	TRUCKS	CAR TYPE
ETS 2001	Alco/GE, 1912	Alco/GE	DE DT locomotive

(Originally Oregon Electric 21, sold to BCER in 1946 as 961, became ETS 2001 in 1980.)

B. Electric Trolley Buses

ELECTRIC TROLLEY BUS	BUILDER AND DATE	SERIAL NUMBER
Edmonton TS 113 *(Originally 116)*	Pullman 44T, 1944	5500
Edmonton TS 148	CCF/Brill T-44, 1947	5040
Edmonton TS 191	CCF/Brill T-44, 1949	5678
Edmonton TS 202	CCF/Brill T-48A, 1954	8345

C. Motor Buses

Edmonton TS 5 (I)	Leyland KPZ-4/Smith, 1939	1376 (Gasoline)
Edmonton TS 5 (II)	GM T6H 4521, 1968	– (Diesel)
Edmonton TS 37	CCF/Brill C-36, 1947	2652 (Gasoline)
Edmonton TS 43	CCF/Brill C-36, 1948	8766 (Gasoline)
Edmonton TS 59	Twin Coach 44SP, 1950	657C (Gasoline)
Edmonton TS 99	Brill C-36, 1946	– (Gasoline)
Edmonton TS 432	GM TDH-5105, 1958	3469 (Diesel)
Edmonton TS 438	GM TDH-5301, 1960	1568 (Diesel)
Edmonton TS (number unknown)	Daimler Fleetline, 1967	36209 (Diesel)

BRITISH COLUMBIA

Nelson

Nelson Electric Tramway Society, PO Box 389, Nelson, BC V1L 5R2. (604) 354-4653. Standard-gauge tourist trolley. Board at Cahko-Mika Mall on the west arm of Kootenay lake or at the car barn in Lakeside Park. Runs daily 10:00 a.m. to 6:00 p.m. from the last two weeks of May until the first week of September, weekends in April, September and first half of October.

Nelson had perhaps the smallest trolley system in North America. Its three cars ran until 1949 and car 23's body survived, latterly as a dog kennel. In the mid-1980s it was cosmetically restored by staff and students of Selkirk Technical College. Thoughts then turned to creating a tourist trolley and the present line opened in 1992. A downtown extension is under review, but won't happen until funding is assured and a way is found to cross the Canadian Pacific's railroad tracks.

CAR	BUILDER AND DATE	TRUCKS	CAR TYPE
Nelson Street Ry. 23	Stephenson, 1906	Brill 39-E replica	SE DT City
(Originally Cleveland, Forest City Ry. 3334, became Cleveland Ry. 934 in 1908, Nelson 3 in 1924, 23 circa 1935.)			
Victoria, BCER 400	Brill, 1921	Brill 79-E-1	DE ST Birney "safety"
(This car is on loan from the Greater Victoria Electric Railway Society.)			

North Vancouver

North Vancouver Museum and Archives, 333 Chesterfield North, Vancouver, BC. (604) 987-5618

The Museum owns the body of British Columbia Electric Railway 155 (Brill, 1908).

Vancouver

1. City of Vancouver City Hall, 453 West 12th, Vancouver, BC V5Y 1V4 (604) 873-7145. Proposed tourist trolley.

In 1991, the city proposed a 3-mile tourist trolley along the south side of False Creek between the Stadium Skytrain station and Granville Island for completion in 1993. The city completed the $C9 million purchase of Canadian Pacific RR's False Creek line for the route in 1995. Tracks run from the Granville bridge to the Cambie bridge in False Creek, linking Granville Island and Science World. Cars stockpiled for use include BCER interurban coaches 1207, 1223 and TTC Type A-6 PCCs 4339, 4352. BCER 1231 (partly dismantled) was bought by the city late in 1996. BC Transit restored BCER interurban 1207 in 1990. The city has leased it from BC Transit for five years, to operate if the line is built, or for static display on Granville Island at a shelter to be built at Moberly Road and Sixth Avenue. However, the vintage cars may be passed over in favor of operating four "modern" cars, plus a fifth as a spare. The project will cost $C27 million. No completion date has been announced, nor has the source for the "modern" cars.

2. Old Spaghetti Factory Restaurant, 53 Water Street, Vancouver, BC. (604) 684-1288.

This restaurant has British Columbia Electric Railway 53 (home-built, 1904, Brill 21-E) as its dining-room centerpiece.

3

3. Vancouver-New Westminster

The body of BCER 153 (Brill, 1908) is at BC Transit's "Skytrain" Maintenance and Control Center, near 22nd Street Skytrain station.

4. Vancouver-Richmond *Cars (ownership unknown) stored at Arrow Transportation, 11580 Mitchell Road, Richmond, BC. (604) 324-1333.*

CAR	BUILDER AND DATE	TRUCKS	CAR TYPE
BCER 960	Alco/GE 1912	Alco/GE	DE DT Locomotive
(Formerly Oregon Electric 22, sold to BCER in 1946.)			
BCER 1220	St. Louis, 1913	St. Louis 23ES	DE DT Interurban coach
(At Trolleyland Electric Railway, Olympia, WA for many years after leaving service in 1958.)			

5. Vancouver-Surrey, *BC Transit, 13401-108 Avenue, Surrey BC V3T 5T4. (604) 540-3000.*

BC Transit, operating rail and bus services throughout the province plus ETBs in Vancouver, stores the following ETBs at the Oakridge Transit Center (Oak and 41st Avenue) in Vancouver.

ELECTRIC TROLLEY BUS	BUILDER AND DATE	SERIAL NUMBER
Vancouver (BCER) 2040	CCF/Brill T44, 1947	5280
Vancouver (BCER) 2416	CCF/Brill T48A, 1954	8339
(This was the last CCF/Brill ETB built.)		

Victoria

Greater Victoria Electric Railway Society, *PO Box 8737, Victoria, BC V8W 3S3. (604) 383-1171.*

The GVERS is a lobby group mandated to protect former railroad rights-of-way for a Greater Victoria light rail system, including a tourist trolley between the Outer Docks and downtown. It owns two streetcars and two buses, kept at a site owned by the Saanich Historical Artifacts Society. Oporto 167 is an approximation of BCER 30, the 1905 home-built original of which had been a similar car running in Victoria BC. It was briefly displayed in the Cloverdale BC museum, stored in Vancouver, then donated by BC Transit to the GVERS in 1993 and shipped to Victoria. The GVERS also owns BCER Birney 400 (on loan to Nelson BC), BC Hydro bus 3404 and BCER bus 3405 (both CCF/Brill, 1957, with UK AEC diesel motors).

The British Columbia Museum in Victoria owns Kitchener PUC (ON) ETB 103 (CCF/Brill T44, 1946, serial number 5013).

MANITOBA

Winnipeg

Winnipeg Metro Transit, *operating city bus services, owns Winnipeg ETB 1768 (CCF/Brill T48A, 1950, serial number 5387).*

NEW BRUNSWICK

Hillsboro Salem and Hillsborough Railroad, *PO Box 70, Hillsboro, NB E0A 1X0. (506) 734-3195 or 734-3100.*

The Salem and Hillsborough Railroad owns six St. John single truck streetcar bodies.

CAR	BUILDER AND DATE	TRUCKS	CAR TYPE
New Brunswick Power 116	Tillsonburg, 1914	—	DE ST City (body only)
(Originally St. John Railway Company 116.)			
New Brunswick Power 132/34/44/46/48	Home-built, 1925 [132], 1928 [144], 1929 [remainder]	—	DE ST City (body only)

Brantford Langford's Restaurant on Highway 2 east of Brantford has Toronto TTC Type A-9 PCC 4560 (originally Cincinnati Street Railway 1160, St. Louis, 1947). Also in Brantford, on a vacant lot at Highway 2 and 403 is Toronto TTC Type A-7 PCC 4427 (St. Louis/CCF, 1949) which after retirement was owned by Langford's Restaurant for some years.

Cornwall On Highway 2, near a Cornwall Transit garage is Cornwall Street Railway Light & Power Electric locomotive 17 (Baldwin/Westinghouse, 1930). This car was originally Salt Lake and Utah 106, then Grand River Ry. 230.

Erin A fast food restaurant at Highway 24 and Union Street has Toronto TTC Type A-6 PCC car 4324 (St. Louis/CCF 1947)

Haileybury Haileybury Fire Museum, Bag D, Haileybury, ON POJ 1KJO (705) 671-1922. Displays Toronto Railway Company single-truck convertible trailer 124 of 1904, sole survivor of 87 cars used for temporary housing after fire destroyed Haileybury in 1921.

Haliburton A boy scout reserve nine miles east of Haliburton has Toronto TTC Type L-1 "Peter Witt" car 2500 (CCF, 1921)

Homey Harbor 26 miles NW of Orillia on Muskoka Road No. 5, five miles west of Highway 69, is the body of Toronto TTC Type Q center-entrance "Peter Witt" trailer 2835 (CCF, 1923)

Orillia 62 miles north of Toronto, the Ossawippi Express Restaurant has London and Port Stanley interurban 4 (Jewett, 1915) as part of a railroad-themed restaurant.

Ottawa

*1. **National Museum of Science and Technology**, 1867 St. Laurent Blvd., Ottawa, ON K1G 5A3. (613) 991-3044. Open daily May-August, Tuesday-Sunday rest of the year.*

The Museum highlights rail transport from Canada's earliest days to the present and occasionally sponsors main-line steam excursions in partnership with the Bytown Railway Society. The streetcars and buses are not on public view.

A. City and Suburban Cars

CARS	BUILDER AND DATE	TRUCKS	CAR TYPE
Ottawa TC 4 (probably)	Stephenson, 1880	Pedestal	SE ST Horse car
(Originally Ottawa City Passenger Railway 7.)			
Toronto Railway Company 16	Stephenson, 1874	Pedestal	SE ST Horse car
(Originally Toronto Street Railway Co. 16.)			
Toronto TTC 64	Jones, 1879	Pedestal	SE ST Type T horse car
(Originally Toronto Street Railway Co. 85, later Toronto Railway Co. 64.)			
Toronto TTC 306	Toronto Ry. Co. 1892	Blackwell	SE ST Type A-1 city
Ottawa TC 854	Ottawa, 1927	CCF 3550	SE DT City
Originally Ottawa Electric Railway 854. At Canadian Railway Museum [Delson PQ] from 1959 to 1971.)			

B. Interurban Cars

BCER 1235	St. Louis, 1913	St. Louis 23ES	DE DT Interurban coach
(At Trolleyland Electric Railway, Olympia, WA 1958-1975.)			

C. Work Cars

Cornwall (ON)	Ottawa, 1926	Pedestal	DE ST Snow Sweeper
Street Railway B-1			
(Originally Ottawa Electric Railway B-1, then Ottawa TC B-1.)			

D. Electric Trolley Buses

BUS	BUILDER AND DATE	SERIAL NUMBER
Montreal MTC 4042	CCF/Brill T44, 1947	5387

E. Motor Buses

Montreal MTC 975	ACF 26s, 1940	160 (Gasoline)
Montreal, Provincial Tnspt.	4756 GM PD-3703, 1947	109 (Diesel)

2. OC Transpo, *St. Laurent bus garage, 1500 St. Laurent Ottawa ON K1A 0MB. Private collection, not open to the public.*

OC Transpo has the body of Ottawa TC 696, originally Ottawa Electric Ry. 603 (Ottawa, 1917), acquired from the Canadian Railway Museum in 1989. OC Transpo also has parts of Ottawa TC 831 (Ottawa, 1924) stored at the Bayswater Avenue Municipal yard.

Rockwood

Ontario Electric Railway Historical Association, PO Box 578, Milton, ON L9T 5AT. (519) 856-9802. Owns and operates the 4' 10 7/8" gauge Halton County Radial Railway Museum at 13629 Guelph Line, Milton, ON. Open daily 10:00 a.m.-5:00 p.m. July and August, Wednesday-Sunday in June, weekends and holidays May-October.

Established in 1953, this was Canada's first trolley museum. A not-for-profit corporation, the OERHA found its present site (part of the former Toronto Suburban Company's Toronto-Guelph Radial [interurban] line, closed in 1931) soon after and vehicles began arriving in 1954. The first car ran on May 24, 1971 and public operation began June 25, 1972. The collection has a heavy emphasis on Toronto but cars from all provinces are collected, plus electric trolley buses and motor buses. Unusually, the line terminates in loops at both ends, so allowing single-end cars to be operated without having to back up.

A. City and Suburban Cars

CAR	BUILDER AND DATE	TRUCKS	CAR TYPE
London (ON) St. Ry. 23	Montreal Park & Island shops, 1901	–	SE DT 15-bench open (body only)
Toronto City Ry. 55	Preston, 1915	Brill 21-E	DE ST City
(Became TTC Type F 2210 in 1921, and used as snow scraper from 1931 to 1954.)			
Oshawa (ON) Ry. 82	Ottawa, 1923	–	DE DT City (body only)
Sandwich, Windsor & Amherstburg 212	Brill, 1922	–	DE ST Birney "safety" (body only)
Guelph (ON) Radial 225	Preston, 1922	–	DE ST Birney "safety" (body only)
(212 and 225 will be used to make one complete Birney car.)			
Toronto Ry. Co. 327	TTC, 1933	Montreal	SE ST 10 bench open (Replica of 1893 car)
Hamilton (ON) St. Ry. 403	Laconia, 1906	–	DE DT City (body only)
(Originally built for a Boston-area company, came to Hamilton in 1908.)			
Toronto TTC 416	Ottawa, 1925	Taylor low-floor	DE DT Type R-1 lightweight suburban
(Originally Ontario Hydro Electric Railway Car.)			
Hamilton (ON) St. Ry. 521	National Steel Car, 1927	–	SE DT City (body only)
Toronto TTC 1326	Toronto Ry. Co., 1910	Curtis D2	SE DT Type BB City
(Originally a convertible car.)			
Toronto Ry. Co. 1704	Home-built, 1913	Curtis 5896	SE ST convertible.
(Was TTC Class E 1704, then rail-grinder W-25 from 1925 until 1962. Being restored as an open car.)			
Toronto TTC 2150	Niles, 1913	–	DE DT Type H-1 city (body only)
(Originally Toronto Civic Rys. 111.)			
Toronto TTC 2395	CCF, 1923	–	DE DT Type N trailer (body only)
Toronto TTC 2424	CCF, 1921	CCF 3265	SE DT Type K-2 Large "Peter Witt" city
Toronto TTC 2786	CCF, 1923	CCF 3550	SE DT Type P-1 Small "Peter Witt" city
Toronto TTC 2890/94	Ottawa, 1923	CCF 3550	SE DT Type P-2 Small "Peter Witt" city
Toronto TTC 2943	CCF, 1923	–	SE DT Type Q Harvey trailer (body only)
Toronto TTC 2984	CCF, 1923	CCF 3265	SE DT Type L-2 Large "Peter Witt" city
Toronto TTC 4000	St. Louis/CCF, 1938	Clark B-2	SE DT Type A-1 PCC
Toronto TTC 4386	St. Louis/CCF, 1948	Clark B-2	SE DT Type A-6 PCC
Toronto TTC 4600 (II), 4611/17	St. Louis/CCF, 1951	Clark B-2	SE DT Type A-15 PCC
(Originally Toronto TTC Type A-8 PCC 4505/40/39 respectively.)			

Toronto TTC 4684	St. Louis, 1946	Clark B-2	SE DT MU Type A-12 PCC

(Originally Louisville Ry. 509, then Cleveland CTS 4259.)

Toronto TTC Type A-7 MU PCC 4426 and Type A-11 PCC 4633 (originally Cleveland CTS 4208) are being used for parts. Toronto TTC Type A-7 MU PCC 4434 has been sold to a Chinese restaurant in an unknown upper-New York State location.

B. Interurban Cars

London & Port Stanley 3	Preston, 1915	–	DE DT Trailer (body only)
London & Port Stanley 8	Jewett, 1915	Baldwin 84-35AA	DE DT Combine
Montreal & So. Co. 107	Ottawa, 1912	Curtis Cl-158-72	DE DT Combine

C. Rapid Transit Cars

TTC 5098, 5099	Gloucester, 1954	Gloucester	SE DT Subway

D. Work Cars and Locomotives

Toronto TTC C-1	Toronto Ry. Co., 1913	Baldwin 78-30A	SE DT 5-ton crane
Lake Erie & Northern M-4	Elec. Ry. Imprvmt. Co., 191	Unknown	Self-propelled rail bonder
Toronto TTC 4	Toronto Ry. Co., 1904	Curtis D-2	SE DT Flat motor
Toronto TTC RT-7	Preston, 1915	Brill 21-E	DE ST subway rail grinder

(Originally Toronto Civic Railways 53, became TTC Type F 2204 in 1921, became scraper in 1932, grinder W-27 in 1955. Transferred to subway in 1967, became RT-7 in 1968.)

Toronto TTC TP-11	National Steel Car, 1946	Baldwin 7520K	SE DT Snow plow
Toronto TTC W-28	Preston, 1917	Brill 21-E	SE ST Rail grinder

(Originally Toronto Civic Railways 57, later TTC Type F 2214, became scraper in 1932 and grinder in 1954.)

Toronto TTC S-37	Russell, 1920	Brill 27-E-1 1/2	DE DT Snow sweeper

(Originally Eastern Mass P-608, later New York TARS 90.)

Oshawa Ry. 45	Niagara, St. Catharine's & Toronto, 1925	Baldwin 3418	SE DT Line car
Lake Erie & Northern 335	Baldwin/WH 1916	Baldwin	DE DT Locomotive

(Later Cornwall Street Railway Light & Power 16.)

E. Electric Trolley Buses

BUS	BUILDER AND DATE	SERIAL NUMBER
Toronto TTC 23	Packard/Brill, 1992	–
Hamilton Street Railway 732	CCF/Brill T48A, 1951	8257
Hamilton Street Railway 765	Flyer E700A, 1972	234
Hamilton Street Railway 7801	Flyer E800, 1978	–

Hamilton 7802 was acquired for parts.

F. Motor Buses

Toronto TTC 792	Ford 69B, 1945	(Gasoline)

(This number is fictitious The bus was from Woodstock ON, later Kitchener 20. Toronto Ford buses were numbered up to 791.)

Brampton (ON) 5741	GM TDH-4512, 1957	2485 (Diesel)

(Originally Hamilton Street Railway 517.)

Toronto

1. **The former Applebee's Restaurant at McCaul Loop** owned Ottawa TC city car 829 *(Ottawa, 1924, CCF 3350 trucks) and the body of Toronto TTC Type P-2 small "Peter Witt" 2806 (Ottawa, 1923). The restaurant closed spring 1996, The cars' future is uncertain.*

2. **Canadian Pacific Railroad's John Street** *roundhouse stores historic rail vehicles for eventual display, including Canadian Railway Historical Association's Toronto TTC Type K Large "Peter Witt" 2300 (CCF, 1921). The car was owned by the Canadian Railway Museum from 1963 until the early 1980s, but never left Toronto.*

3. **Canadian Transit Heritage Foundation,** *PO Box 30, Toronto ON M5A 1N1. (416) 365-9800. The CTHF is a federally incorporated non-profit group formed in 1992 and dedicated to preserving Canada's urban transit heritage.*

4. **Toronto Transportation Commission,** *1900 Yonge Street, Toronto ON M4S 1Z2 (416) 393-4000.*

The TTC since 1920 has been the main transit provider for Toronto. Its last PCC cars ran in December 1995. The TTC maintains a small fleet of historic vehicles. They are not on public view, but are available for occasional charter trips.

CAR	BUILDER AND DATE	TRUCKS	CAR TYPE
Toronto TTC 2766	CCF, 1923	CCF 3550	SE DT Type P-1 small "Peter Witt" city
Toronto TTC 4500/49	St. Louis/CCF, 1951	Clark B-2	SE DT Type A-15 PCC
Toronto TTC W-30, W-31	Pullman, 1946	Clark B-2	SE DT MU PCC rail grinders

(Originally Cleveland TS 4206, 4243, Toronto TTC type A-11 MU PCC 4631, 4668 from 1952, became rail grinders in 1974/75.)

QUEBEC

Montreal

Delson-St. Constant Canadian Railway Museum, *120 St. Pierre St., Saint-Constant PQ J5A 2G9. (514) 632-2410. Standard-gauge railroad and trolley museum. Open daily 9:00 a.m.-5:00 p.m. May-August, weekends in September and October.*

Canada's greatest collection of vintage rail artifacts, the CRM was established in the early 1960s. Though primarily a static national rail museum, the street railway collection is largely from the Montreal area. Most are operational and a mile of track circling the museum complex was opened in the 1970s.

A. City and Suburban Cars

CAR	BUILDER AND DATE	TRUCKS	CAR TYPE
Montreal Tramways 1, 3	Home-built, 1905, 1924	Brill 27-G	SE DT Observation
(Car 3 loaned to Heritage Park, Calgary between 1977 and 1989.)			
Ottawa TC 6	Ottawa, 1895	Unknown	DE ST City
Interprovincial Railway 8	Patterson & Corbin, 1895	Unknown	DE ST 10-bench open
(Originally Peterborough [ON] & Ashburton Street Railway car, became Toronto Suburban Railway 18 in 1918.)			
New Brunswick Power 82	Ottawa, 1906	Unknown	DE ST City
(Originally St. John Railway 82.)			
Montreal Tramways 200 (II)	Brill, 1921	Brill 79-E-1	DE ST Birney "safety"
(Formerly Detroit DSR 223.)			
Montreal Tramways 274	Newburyport, 1894	Unknown	SE ST City
(Became a salt car in 1911.)			
Montreal Tramways 350	Brownell, 1892	Unknown	SE ST City
(Montreal's first electric car and one of the first built with Brownell's patented "Accelerator" bulkhead doors giving separate entrance and exit to the passenger compartment.)			
Ottawa TC 423	Ottawa, 1906	Unknown	SE ST Mail car
Montreal Tramways 859	Brill, 1907	Brill 27-G	SE DT Semi-convertible
Ottawa TC 859	Ottawa, 1928	Unknown	SE DT City
Montreal Tramways 997	Ottawa, 1910	Brill 27-F-E-2	SE DT Semi-convertible
Montreal Tramways 1046	Home-built, 1902	Canada Switch & Signal Type 40	SE DT Suburban
(Originally a Montreal Park and Island car. Drastically rebuilt in 1924.)			
Montreal Tramways 1317/39	Ottawa, 1913	Brill 27-G-E-2	SE DT City
Montreal Tramways 1801	CCF, 1924	Unknown	SE DT City
Montreal Tramways 1953/59	CCF, 1928	Unknown	SE DT Lightweight
(Car 1953 owned by Donald F. Angus of Senneville Que. from 1963 until acquisition by the museum.)			
Montreal Tramways 2222	CCF, 1929	Unknown	SE DT Lightweight
Montreal Tramways 3517	St. Louis/CCF 1944	Clark B-2	SE DT PCC

An unidentified 1880 Stephenson horsecar (either Quebec Street Railway [Lower Town] or St. John Street Railway [Upper Town]) is in the collection.

B. Interurban Cars

London & Port Stanley 10	Jewett, 1915	Baldwin 84-35A	SE DT Interurban coach
London & Port Stanley 14	Jewett, 1917	Unknown	SE DT Interurban coach
Montreal & So. Co. 104	Ottawa, 1912	Curtis CI-158-72	SE DT Interurban coach

Quebec Railway Light & Power 105 *(Originally Quebec, Montmorency & Charlevoix 105.)*	Jackson & Sharp, 1889	Unknown	DE DT Combine trailer
Quebec Ry. Lt. & Pwr 401	Ottawa, 1901	Unknown	SE DT Interurban coach
Montreal & So. Co. 611 *(Numbered 606 until 1927.)*	Ottawa, 1917	Taylor	SE DT Interurban coach

C. Work Cars and Locomotives

Montreal Tramways W-2	Home-built, 192	Unknown	DE DT Crane
Montreal Tramways Y-5 *(Originally a sludge car.)*	Home-built, 1912	Unknown	DE ST Shop switcher "Charlie"
Toronto TTC TP-10	National Steel Car, 1945	Unknown	DE DT Snow Plow
Montreal Tramways 51 *(Originally Three Rivers [PQ] Traction Co. car.)*	Ottawa, 1928	Unknown	DE ST Snow sweeper
Montreal Tramways 3151	CCF, 1925	Unknown	SE DT Motor flat
Montreal Tramways 3200	Home-built, 1928	Unknown	DE DT Tool car
Montreal Tramways 5001	Home-built, 1917	Unknown	DE DT Locomotive

Montreal Tramways ETB 4067 (CCF/Brill T44, 1950, serial number 5841) is owned by the Urban Community Transit Commission in Montreal. It is not on public display.

SASKATCHEWAN

Moose Jaw

History of Transportation, 50 Diefenbaker Drive, Moose Jaw, SASK S6H 4N8. (306) 693-5989.

Saskatchewan's Western Development Museum has four branches, each a sophisticated professional museum in its own right, dealing with a different theme in the development of Canada's Western Prairie. "Boomtown 1910" is at 2610 Lorne Avenue South Saskatoon S7J 0S6, "Story of People" is at Highway 16 West Yorktown S3N 2V6 and "Heritage Farm and Village" is at Highways 16 and 40 North Brattleford S9A 2Y1. The "History of Transportation" museum is a comprehensive overview of transport on Canada's western prairies, from the early 19th century with its water and animal transport, to today, with automotive and airborne vehicles.

There are several significant railroad exhibits, plus Saskatoon Municipal Railway double-truck streetcar 61 (Ottawa, 1929) and Saskatoon TS ETB 177 (CCF/Brill T48A, 1951, serial number – 8243). Saskatoon snowsweeper 200 and Saskatoon "Peter Witt" car 202, once owned by the museum, were sold to the Edmonton Radial Railway Society.

The city of Regina owns Regina TS ETB 128 (CCF/Brill T44, 1949, serial number 5656).

A heavily-rebuilt PCC car of the Fort Worth subway about to plunge into the tunnel which will bring it to the Tandy Center terminal on June 5, 1992.

New Orleans car 933 outward bound to Lee Circle from Canal Street on February 13, 1993.

McKinney Avenue Transit Authority Birney car 636 begins another trip back to downtown Dallas in May 1991.

10

A Chicago corner at the Illinois Railway museum in September 1988. The station building is from the Chicago El, as is articulated PCC rapid transit car 52. Chicago PCC streetcar 4391 is on the right.

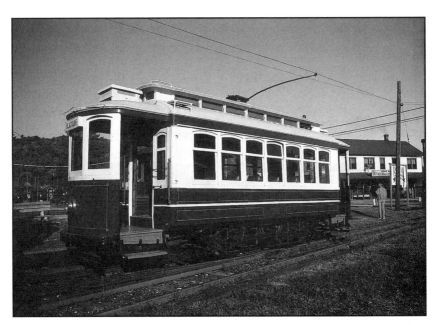

In September, 1992 Rockhill Trolley Museum's ex-Porto car 172 waits for arriving passengers from the East Broad Top railroad, whose station building is in the right background.

11

UNITED STATES

ARIZONA

Phoenix

Arizona Historical Society, Central Arizona Chapter, 1300 North College Avenue, Tempe, AZ 85281. (602) 929-0292.

In the 1980s, the AHS restored Phoenix Street Railway 116 (American, 1929) a double-truck Birney "safety" car, hoping to run it on 250 yards of track in a linear park next to a freeway. Car is at 1242 N. Central, Phoenix AZ 85008. More information from Larry Fleming, 2929 N. 44 Street, Phoenix, AZ 85008. Toronto Type A-15 PCC car 4607 (originally Toronto TTC Type A-8 4536) was bought by Phoenix Transit System (ATC/Vancom) in January 1996 for a history exhibit at a new transit center. The car promotes a light rail proposal, to include either a tourist trolley component or a tourist trolley line as a central area circulator. It may make demonstration runs on a short length of track. Information from PTS, 302 North 1st Avenue, Phoenix AZ 85008.

Tucson

Old Pueblo Trolley, Box 1373, Tucson, AZ. 85702 (602) 792-1802. Standard-gauge tourist trolley. Runs weekends all year.

Created to return trolleys to University Boulevard as part of the University of Arizona's centennial celebration, the OPT (a member of the Arizona Historical Society) has run cars in Tucson since April 17, 1993. The University Boulevard trackage is original. A downtown extension and turning loops, to allow the single-end Toronto PCC to run, are planned.

A. City and Suburban Cars

CAR	BUILDER AND DATE	TRUCKS	CAR TYPE
LARY 860	American, 1913	–	DE DT Type B-1 city (body only)
(This 3'6" gauge car will be restored to working order using standard-gauge parts from Osaka car 254.)			
Kyoto, (Japan) 869	Umebachi/Sharyo, 1953	Brill 77-E	DE DT City
(Became Hankai Tramway of Nankai Electric Ry., Osaka 255 in 1972.)			
Brussels, (Belgium) MIVB/STIB 1511 (1048)	Home-built, 1936	Brussels Brill 21-E	SE ST City
Toronto TTC 4608	St. Louis/CCF, 1951	Clark B-2	SE DT Type A-15 PCC
(Originally Toronto TTC Type A-8 4544.)			

Old Pueblo Birney "safety" car 10 (American, 1918) (originally PE 332) went back to the Orange Empire Railway Museum in 1995. A 1937 Minneapolis Yellow Coach Type 733 came from the Minnesota Transportation Museum in 1996 to restore a similar Tucson vehicle.

ARKANSAS

Fort Smith

Fort Smith Streetcar Restoration Association, 2121 Wolfe Lane, Fort Smith, AR 72901. (501) 783-0205. Operates standard gauge trolley daily May-October, weekends November-April. Board car at Cemetery Gates, Trolley Museum, Rogers or Garrison.

The museum began in 1979 when the FSSRA was set up to preserve and exhibit city transit history. Car 224 first ran May 19, 1991 on 1/4 mile of former St. Louis & San Francisco RR freight sidings, terminating opposite the Fort Smith National Historic site. In 1994, car 224 was named to the National Register of Historic Places to recognize its significance in Forth Smith's transit history. In the same year, the line was extended 1/4 mile to the National Cemetery Gates, and to Garrison Avenue on August 29, 1996.

A. City and Suburban Cars

CAR	BUILDER AND DATE	TRUCKS	CAR TYPE
Vera Cruz 6	Brill, 1907	Brill 21-E	DE ST 10-bench open
(Acquired 1995 from Texas Transportation Museum, San Antonio.)			
Fort Smith Traction Light & Power 10	American, 1902	–	DE ST City (body only)
Hot Springs (AR) St. Ry. 50	St. Louis, 1904	–	DE DT City (body only)
Fort Smith Light & Traction 205	Cincinnati, 1919	–	DE ST Birney "safety" (body only)
Fort Smith Light & Traction 221	American, 1926	–	DE ST Birney "safety" (body only)
(Car 221 sold as a house on Fort Smith trolley closure in 1933, donated to museum 1994. Car will stay as a house to illustrate Depression conditions in Arkansas.)			
Fort Smith Light & Traction 224	American, 1926	Brill 79-E-1	DE ST Birney "safety"
Kansas City PS 1545	American, 1919	Brill 79-E-1	DE ST Birney "safety"
(Acquired from the Ohio Railway Museum, Worthington, OH.)			

B. Motor Buses

BUS	BUILDER AND DATE	SERIAL NUMBER
Little Rock (AR) Capital Tnsptn. 132	Twin Coach R-23, 1939	– (Gasoline)
Fort Smith 285	GM TGH-3102, 1954	235 (Gasoline)
(Originally TCRT [MN] 100. Now in Army drab after use in the Neil Simon movie "Biloxi Blues" filmed at nearby Fort Chaffee.)		
Oklahoma City Bus Co 281	GM TGH-3101, 1951 335	– (Gasoline)

CALIFORNIA

Dunmovin

Inyo County, *near China Lake, Bubonic Plague Acres. 3' 6" gauge private trolley line, not open to the public.*

LARY PCC 3072 (St. Louis, 1938, Clark B-1 trucks) was bought in 1963 by Jack Richter, who began running it in 1970 on a few hundred feet of track next to U.S. Highway 395. A generator feeds 18 automobile batteries which power the car.

Lake Tahoe

Tahoe Airport Generic Rail *(Gunnar Henrioulle), PO Box 9289, South Lake Tahoe, CA 96158. (916) 541-2959. Private collection, open to the public only by prior arrangement.*

This collection is the heart of Gunnar Henrioulle's visionary plan for transit alternatives to Lake Tahoe's crowded highways. Light rail is envisaged between Tahoe City (on the north shore) and Truckee, using former Southern Pacific RR tracks. Trackage rights on the SP between Truckee and Reno-Sparks and on to Reno Cannon Airport (and ultimately Carson City) will be obtained for high-technology rail transit. The Reno-Sparks/Airport segment will also be used by a new light rail line. Tahoe City to Camp Richardson on the south shore will be linked by ferry. South Shore light rail lines will run from Camp Richardson to Lake Tahoe Airport and Myers, with a branch from the airport to Ski Run Marina in South Lake Tahoe and Stateline. The project's first segment forsees vintage light rail between Lake Tahoe Airport and Camp Richardson. Henrioulle has worked on these plans since 1975 to promote and demonstrate renewable energy sources in railcars and locomotives. This roster is incomplete. (* = 3' 6" gauge.)

A. City and Suburban Cars

CAR	BUILDER AND DATE	TRUCKS	CAR TYPE
Sacramento Gas & Electric 36	American, 1913	–	DE DT "California" (body only)
San Diego ER 502	St. Louis, 1937	Clark B-2	DE DT PCC car

A. City and Suburban Cars, *continued*

Later El Paso City Lines 1500, sold to San Diego Electric Railway Association in the 1980s, partly damaged by fire in 1996, sold to Lake Tahoe later in 1996.)

San Francisco MUNI 1024/26-28/34/35	St. Louis, 1951	St. Louis B-3	DE DT PCC
San Francisco MUNI 1101/05/11/13/22/23/27/34/35/42/45/48/69/70	St. Louis, 1946	Clark B-2	DE DT PCC

(Originally St. Louis PS 1700/06/07/22/16/28/05/48/60/08/23/29/78/77 respectively)

*LARY 1435	St. Louis, 1924	LA Ry. T-5(B)	DE DT Type H-3 city

This car was at the Orange Empire Museum, Perris CA., then sold for parts to MSR of San Francisco in 1990.)

Toronto TTC 4404/72	St. Louis/CCF 1949	Clark B-2	SE DT MU Type A-7 PCC

Fremont

Society for the Preservation of Carter Railroad Resources, *PO Box 783, Newark, CA 94560. (510) 797-9557. 3'6" gauge horse RR museum at 34600 Ardenwood Blvd. (I-880 and highway 84) 15 miles south of Oakland. Cars run Thursday-Sunday, April-October.*

The SPCRR's horse railroad serves the 200-acre Ardenwood Historic Farm, an open-air park recreating farm life of the 1890s. The SPCRR collects and preserves wood-bodied vehicles of Carter Brothers, Newark CA. builders of railroad passenger and freight cars, and streetcars for local area customers. Several of San Francisco's Powell Street cable cars are nominally Carter-built vehicles, though they have been rebuilt so many times in their century-plus of life that little of the original now remains. The restoration shop, which uses woodworking tools and techniques of the 1880s, is open to the public. Restored cars are hauled by the Society's horses on a recreation of the old South Pacific Coast Railroad's Centerville branch, horse-powered for more than twenty-five years in the 19th century. The SPCRR also owns Oakland Railroad 8 (Carter, 1885), a city horse car.

Los Angeles

1. Petersen Automotive Museum, *6060 Wilshire Blvd., Los Angeles, CA 90036. (213) 930-2277.*

The Petersen Automotive Museum owns Oporto 198 (CCFP, 1935), split in half to simulate two streetcars on the same track, with ends modified to look like LARY Type B cars. The display is part of a diorama recreating a scene from the Laurel and Hardy movie *Hog Wild* (Hal Roach studios, 1930), filmed on Bonnie Brae Street in Los Angeles.

2. Los Angeles County Metropolitan Transportation Authority, *818 W. Seventh Street, Los Angelesm CA 90017. (213) 623-1194.*

LACMTA succeeded the Southern California Rapid Transit District in 1993 as the rapid transit, light rail and bus provider of Los Angeles County. It also took over the SCRTD's historic bus collection. These vehicles are not on public view.

BUS	BUILDER AND DATE	SERIAL NUMBER
LAMTA 663	GM TDH-4801, 1958	500 (Diesel)
PE 2700	GM TDH-4510, 1948	501 (Diesel)
PE 2875	GM TDH-5103, 1951	577 (Diesel)
St. Louis PS 3258	GM TDH-4507, 1947	759 (Diesel)
SCRTD 4002	Flxible 411-GD-CZ, 1966	75032 (Diesel)
LAMTA 5009	GM TDH-5303, 1963	173 (Diesel)
LAMTA 5251	GM TDH-5301, 1961	2113 (Diesel)
LAMTA 5300	GM TDH-5301, 1959	473 (Diesel)
LAMTA 5721, 5800, 5999	Flxible F2D6V-401-1, 1961/2/3	– (Diesel) 51224, 51502, 51731
SCRTD 7103	Flxible III-C3-1, 1971	54895 (Diesel)

3. Travel Town RR, *Griffith Park 3900 W. Chevy Chase Drive, Los Angeles, CA 90039. Museum at 5200 Zoo Drive, Los Angeles, CA 90039. (213) 662-5874. Static railroad museum. Open daily (except Christmas Day) 10:00 a.m.-4:00 p.m.*

Travel Town was founded in 1952 to collect railroad and other forms of obsolete transport. This roster is incomplete. (* = 3'6"gauge)

CAR	BUILDER AND DATE	TRUCKS	CAR TYPE
*San Francisco MUNI Cal. Cable 21	Unknown	Home-built arch bar	DE DT "California" cable car
*LARY 536	St. Louis, 1906	LA Ry. T-3	DE DT Type B "California"
LAMTA 1543	ACF, 1911	Baldwin 84-30AA	DE DT "Blimp" Interurban coach

(Originally Southern Pacific [Oakland, Alameda, Berkeley lines] 379, then Interurban Electric Railway 379, requisitioned by U.S. Maritime Commission 1942 and sent to PE, became USMC 4640, bought by PE in 1946 as PE 435, became LAMTA 1543 in 1958.)

Perris

Orange Empire Railway Museum, PO Box 548, Perris, CA 92572-0548. (909) 943-3020. Standard and 3' 6" gauge trolley museum at D Street, 1 mile south of Perris. Cars run weekends year-round, daily at certain times of the year 11:00 a.m.- 5:00 p.m.

The museum was formed in 1975 by the merger of the Orange Empire Trolley Museum (founded March 1956) and the California Southern Railroad Museum (founded December 1955). It has a superb Southern California mass transit collection (unduplicated anywhere else in North America), a regional railroad collection, and Ward Kimball's unique Grizzly Flats narrow-gauge railroad. The trolley museum moved here in 1958 and the first car ran in 1960. There is considerable mixed-gauge operation, but generally standard-gauge cars run on the main line (which will soon reach the Perris RR station), while narrow-gauge Los Angeles cars serve the loop around the museum's central core.

Los Angeles Railway trucks were arch-bar designs (both home and commercially built), except: T-5(A) = St. Louis M-N71, T-5(B) = St. Louis M-N69, T-10 = St. Louis EIBN-66, T-11 = Clark B-1 PCC, T-24 special grinder truck.)   (* = 3'6"gauge)

A. City & Suburban Cars

CARS	BUILDER AND DATE	TRUCKS	CAR TYPE
Gt. N. Ry. (Eire) Hill of Howth 2	Brush, 1901	Brill 22-E	DE DT Open-top double-deck city
Bakersfield & Kern (CA) 4	Holman, 1900	Brill 21-E	DE ST "California"
*LARY 7	St. Louis, 1895	–	DE DT Type A "California" (body only)
Tucson (AZ) RT 10 (originally PE 322)	Brill, 1918	Brill 78-M-1-F	DE ST Birney "safety"
*Kyoto, (Japan) 19	Umebachi Iron Works of Sakai (Osaka) circa 1913	Brill 21-E	DE ST City
(Original number and year of build unknown. Numbered 19 in 1956, five years before Kyoto closed.)			
*San Francisco MUNI Cal. Cable 43	Home-built, 1907	Home-built arch-bar	DE DT "California" cable car
Fresno (CA) 51	St. Louis, 1913	–	DE DT "Hobbleskirt" stepless center-entrance (body only)
*Denver Tramways 79	Woeber, 1906	–	DE DT Center-entrance city (body only)
Fresno (CA) 83	St. Louis, 1925	–	DE DT Birney "safety" (body only)
*LARY 151	St. Louis, 1898	LARY T-9	DE DT Type B3 "California"
San Francisco MUNI 162	Jewett, 1914	Baldwin L	DE DT Type B city
Key System (CA) 167	Bethlehem, 1937	Commonwealth	DE DT articulated "Bridge" center-entrance suburban
San Diego ER 167	McGuire-Cummings, 1914	–	DE DT Center-entrance city (body only)
San Francisco MUNI 171	Bethlehem, 1923	Standard 0-50	DE DT Type K city
PE 179	Pullman, 1912	–	DE DT Center-entrance city (body only)
(Originally Southern Pacific [Oakland, Alameda, Berkeley lines] 819.)			
San Diego ER 316	American, 1920	–	DE ST Birney "safety" (body only)
PE 331	Brill, 1918	Brill 78-M-1-F	DE ST Birney "safety"
San Diego ER 508	St. Louis, 1936	Clark B-2	SE DT PCC
PE 511	St. Louis, 1901	–	DE DT Suburban (body only)
(Originally PE 211, became 511 in 1911.)			
PE 524	St. Louis, 1902	–	DE DT Suburban (body only)
Originally PE 224, became 524 in 1911. Bought from the Fellows collection in 1996.)			
*LARY 525	St. Louis, 1906	LARY T-3	DE DT Type BG "California"
San Diego ER 528	St. Louis, 1938	Clark B-2	SE DT PCC

15

A. City & Suburban Cars, *continued*

PE 538	St. Louis, 1909	–	DE DT Suburban (body only)
(Originally PE 238, became PE 538 in 1911.)			
PE 637	St. Louis, 1922	St. Louis M-72	DE DT "Hollywood" suburban
(Became PE 5112 in 1949, became LAMTA 1801 in 1958.)			
PE 655	St. Louis, 1924	–	DE DT "Hollywood" suburban
(Became PE 5094 in 1949, acquired by Richard Fellows circa 1958, put on rubber tires and partially restored, donated to OERM by Mrs. Fellows and the Fellows collection in 1996.)			
*LARY 665	St. Louis, 1911	LARY T-9	DE DT Type B "California"
PE 717	Brill, 1925	St. Louis M-72	DE DT "Hollywood" suburban
(Became 5167 in 1949, became LAMTA 1815 in 1958.)			
*LARY 744, 807	St. Louis, 1911	–	DE DT Type B1 "California" (body only)
*LARY 836	American, 1912	–	DE DT Type B2 "California" (body only)
New Orleans PSI 913	Perley Thomas, 1923	Brill 76-E-2	DE DT Lightweight city
*LARY 936	St. Louis, 1914	–	DE DT Type C "Sowbelly" center-entrance (body only)
*LARY 1003	American, 1920	–	DE ST Type G Birney "safety" (body only)
San Diego ER 1003	American, 1913	–	DE DT City (body only)
(Originally Utah Light & Power [Salt Lake City] car.)			
San Francisco MUNI 1039	St. Louis, 1952	St. Louis B-3	SE DT PCC
*LARY 1160	Home-built, 1923	LARY T-3	DE DT Type F city
(Originally PE 154 [American, 1898], later PE 811, LARY 18 in 1910, rebuilt as LARY 1160 in 1923.)			
*LARY 1201	St. Louis, 1921	LARY T-5(A)	DE DT Type H-4 city
*LARY 1423, 1450	St. Louis, 1924	LARY T-5(B)	DE DT Type H-3 city
*LARY 1559	Home-built, 1925	LARY T-5(B)	DE DT Type K-4 city
*LARY 2601	St. Louis, 1930	LARY T-10	DE DT Type M "Peter Witt" city
*LARY 3001	St. Louis, 1937	LARY T-11	SE DT Type P PCC
*LARY 3100	St. Louis, 1943	LARY T-11	SE DT Type P2 PCC
*LAMTA 3165	St. Louis, 1948	LARY T-11	SE DT Type P3 PCC
PE 5123, 5166	St. Louis, 1922	St. Louis M-72	DE DT "Hollywood" suburban
(Originally numbered 626, 716. Became PE 5123, 5166 in 1949, LAMTA 1812, 1814 in 1958)			
*LARY "Descanso"	Home-built, 1909	–	DE DT Funeral car (body only)

An unidentified horse car (possibly Stephenson, 1880) was bought from Knott's Berry Farm (Anaheim) in 1985. An unidentified horse car (possibly Pasadena 2, possibly Brownell & White, 1875) is in the collection. San Diego ER 88 and 93 (home-built, 1910, DE DT "California" bodies) were destroyed by fire July 6, 1992. LARY Type P PCC 3084 (body only) is unaccessioned and used for storage.

B. Interurban and Electric Freight Cars

Bamberger RR (UT) 127	Brill, 1932	Brill 89-E-1	DE DT "Bullet" interurban
(Originally Fonda, Johnstown & Gloversville [NY] 127.)			
Visalia Electric (CA) 301, 302	American, 1908	–	DE DT Trailer (body only)
(Became PE 1047 and 1046 respectively in 1919, 1047 renumbered 1045 later.)			
PE 314	St. Louis, 1930	St. Louis M-87	DE DT "Blimp" interurban coach
(Originally Northwestern Pacific [Marin County, CA] 384, PE 4509 in 1942, PE 314 in 1947.)			
PE 418	Pullman, 1913	Baldwin 84-30AA	DE DT "Blimp" interurban coach
(Originally Southern Pacific [Oakland, Alameda & Berkeley lines] 344, then Interurban Electric Railway 344, requisitioned by U.S. Maritime Commission 1942 and sent to PE, bought by PE 1944 as 4614, became PE 418 in 1947 and LAMTA 1528 in 1958.)			
Portland, Eugene & Eastern 485	Pullman, 1921	Unknown	DE DT Control trailer
(Later became Northwestern Pacific [Marin County, CA] 217, later became a Southern Pacific RR caboose.)			
PE 498	Pullman, 1913	Baldwin 84-30AA	DE DT "Blimp" Interurban combine
(Originally Southern Pacific [Oakland, Alameda & Berkeley lines] 627, then Interurban Electric Railway 627, requisitioned by U.S. Maritime Commission 1942 and sent to PE, became USMC 27 in 1943, USMC 302 in 1944, bought by PE in 1946 as 4702, became PE 498 in 1947 and LAMTA 1546 in 1958.)			
PE 993	St. Louis, 1907	–	DE DT Interurban coach (body only)
(Originally Los Angeles Pacific 743, became 993 in 1924. Bought from Fellows collection in 1996.)			
PE 1000, 1001	St. Louis, 1913	Brill 27-MCB-3X (1001)	DE DT Interurban coach
(1000 rebuilt into private car "Commodore." Now a body only. 1001 became rail grinder 00199 in 1948.)			
BCER 1225	St. Louis, 1913	St. Louis 23ES	DE DT Interurban coach

| PE 1440 | Home-built, 1910 | – | DE DT Express Motor (body only) |
| PE 1498 | St. Louis, 1904 | – | DE DT Express car (body only) |

(Originally PE 2228, later 338 then 801. Body destroyed by fire July 6, 1992.)

C. Work Cars and Locomotives

American Smelting and Refining Co. 1	Westinghouse, 1912	Unknown	SE ST Mine locomotive
Hutchinson & Nthn. Ry. (KS) 1	GE, 1921	GE Frameless	SE ST Steeple-cab locomotive
PE 008 (II)	Brill, 1913	Baldwin	DE DT Wrecker

(Originally Portland, Eugene 7 Western RPO mail/baggage car 452, later Southern Pacific (Oregon & California) 772, PE box motor 1450 in 1929, PE RPO mail/baggage car 1406 in 1936 and wrecker 008 in 1953.)

PE 00150	Los Angeles Pacific, 1899	St. Louis 23B	DE DT Trolley greaser

(Originally Los Angeles Pacific Tower car 3, became PE 1710 in 1911, 00150 in 1931, trolley greaser in 1936.)

PE 00157 (Originally 1730)	Home-built, 1915	Standard C-80B	DE DT Tower car
Union Pacific, Yakima VT (WA) 297	Baldwin/WH, 1922	Unknown	DE DT Locomotive

(Originally Glendale & Montrose [CA] 2.)

Sacramento Nthn. (CA) 653	GE, 1928	GE 105A	DE DT Steeple-cab locomotive
PE 1624	Home-built, 1925	Home-built	DE DT locomotive
*LARY 9007	American, 1921	–	DE ST Money car (body only)

(Originally Type G Birney "safety" car 1069.)

*LARY 9209	Home-built, 1913	LARY T-3	DE DT Motorized flat
*LARY 9225	Home-built, 1912	LARY T-3	DE DT Rail derrick
*LARY 9310	Home-built, 1925	LARY T-24	DE ST Rail grinder
*LARY 9350, 9351	Home-built, 1907	LARY T-3	DE DT Tower car

(Car 9351 originally numbered 9202.)

*LARY 9550	Home-built, 1904	Brill 21-E	DE ST Shop Switcher
*LAMTA 9614, 9615	Home-built, 1907/1908	LARY T-1	DT Unmotored flat

D. Electric Trolley Buses

BUS	BUILDER AND DATE	SERIAL NUMBER
San Francisco MUNI 530, 536	Marmon-Herrington TC-40, 1948	10420, 10426
San Francisco MUNI 614	Twin Coach 44TTW, 1949	045
Seattle Metro 631 (Originally 884)	Twin Coach 41GWFT, 1940	75218
Seattle Metro 656 (Originally 1006)	Pullman-Standard 44CX, 1944	5528
LAMTA 8002	ACF-Brill TC44, 1945	150

(Originally delivered to Key System for use in Oakland but sold unused to Los Angeles in 1946.)

E. Motor Buses

Chicago Motor Coach 103	Yellow Coach Model 706, 193	001 (Gasoline)
LARY 1501	Yellow Coach Type Z-L-210, 1927	1331 (Gasoline)

San Francisco MUNI gas bus 0163 (Twin Coach 44D, 1947 serial number 147) is on loan to the Market Street Railway San Francisco.)

Rio Vista Junction

Western Railway Museum, 5848 State Highway 12, Suisun City, CA 94585. (707) 374-2978. Standard-gauge trolley museum of the Bay Area Electric Railroad Association. Cars run weekends and holidays year-round 11:00 a.m.- 5:00 p.m.

The BAERA was founded in 1946 to memorialize Northern California's interurbans. It had no permanent home until this site was acquired in 1960. The first cars ran in 1966. For twenty years this was a trolley museum, with some railroad exhibits. Museum rail excursions north to Jepson Prairie on adjacent former Sacramento Northern interurban trackage (built in 1917), began in the 1980s. A hope that this line could be bought and re-electrifed was realized in 1993 when twenty miles was purchased. Three miles from the museum south to Blacklock has been electrified and ultimately the whole line will be done, so making the WRM's demonstration trackage the longest of its kind in North America and a fit place for interurban cars to show their paces. (*= 3'6" gauge.)

A. City and Suburban Cars

CAR	BUILDER AND DATE	TRUCKS	CAR TYPE
Saskatoon MUNI 12	St. Louis, 1915	St. Louis 9	DE ST "Stone & Webster" city
*San Francisco, Sacramento-Clay 20	Unknown, circa 1885	–	DE DT Cable car
(Acquired in 1996 by the Friends of the Cable Car Museum from a group in Medford, OR.)			
Presidio & Ferries Ry. Co. (SF) 28	Hammond, 1895	Peckham 9A	DE ST "California"
(Originally United RR of San Francisco 755, became MUNI type G car 317 in 1915, MUNI C-4 in 1922.)			
Sacramento, Pacific Gas & Electric 41, 46	American, 1918, 1920	–	DE ST Birney "safety" (body only)
Stockton (CA) Electric RR 56	St. Louis, 1920	–	DE ST Birney "safety" (body only)
Sacramento Northern (Chico, CA) 62	American, 1920	Brill 79-E-1	DE ST Birney "safety"
(Originally San Diego ER 301.)			
Sacramento, Pacific Gas & Electric 63	American, 1929	–	DE ST City (body only)
San Francisco MUNI 178	Bethlehem, 1923	–	DE DT Type K city
Key System (CA) 182, 186, 187	Bethlehem, 1937	Commonwealth	DE DT articulated "Bridge" center-entrance suburban
Blackpool Corporation (England) 226	English Electric, 1934	English Electric 4'	DE DT Open "Boat" car
(Renumbered 601 in 1968.)			
Key System (CA) 271	St. Louis, 1901	St. Louis 23A	DE DT City
(Originally Lehigh Valley [PA] 139, was Oakland Traction Co. 251 by 1905.)			
Key System (CA) 352	St. Louis, 1912	Brill 77-E-1	DE DT City
(Originally Oakland Traction Co. 352.)			
Melbourne (Australia) M&MTB 648	Home-built, 1930	Melbourne Type 1	DE DT Type W2 drop-center city
Key System (CA) 987	Home-built, 1927	Brill 77-E-1	DE DT City car
(Originally Key System 899, later became Portland Traction [OR] 4011.)			
San Francisco MUNI 1003	St. Louis, 1939	Brill 97-ER-1 "Brilliner"	DE DT Type C "Magic Carpet"
San Francisco MUNI 1016	St. Louis, 1951	St. Louis B-3	SE DT PCC
San Diego ER 1043	Brill, 1905	Brill 39-E	DE DT Semi-convertible
(Originally a New York Rys. car, then New York TARS 436.)			
San Francisco MUNI 1153	St. Louis, 1946	Clark B-2	SE DT PCC
(Originally St. Louis PS 1742.)			
San Francisco MUNI 1190	St. Louis, 1947	Clark B-2	SE DT PCC
(Originally Kansas City PS 551, became Toronto TTC type A-14 PCC 4752 in 1957, sold to MUNI in 1974.)			
San Francisco MSR	St. Louis, 1901	Brill 27-G	DE DT Private car "

B. Interurban and Electric Freight Cars

Central California Traction 7	Brill, 1929	Baldwin 90-40A	DE DT Box motor
(Originally Washington, Baltimore & Annapolis 1.)			
Peninsular Ry. (CA) 52	American, 1903	Brill 27-MCB-3	DE DT Interurban coach
(Originally San Jose-Los Gatos Ry. 4)			
Peninsular Ry. (CA) 61	American, 1913	–	DE DT Trailer (body only)
(Originally San Jose-Los Gatos Ry. 13.)			
Petaluma & Santa Rosa (CA) 63	Holman, 1904	Brill 27-MCB-2X	DE DT Combine
San Francisco & Napa Valley 63	St. Louis, 1932	Baldwin 84-30B	DE DT Combine
San Francisco & Napa Valley 100	McGuire-Cummings, 1922	Baldwin 84-30B	DE DT Box motor
Cedar Rapids & Iowa City 111	Cincinnati, 1930	Cincinnati AABC74D	SE DT Lightweight interurban coach
(Originally Cincinnati & Lake Erie 111.)			
Tidewater Southern (Stockton CA) 200	Jewett, 1912	–	DE DT Combine (body only)
Indiana RR 202	Kuhlman, 1926	Brill 177-E-1X	DE DT Lightweight interurban coach
(Later Portland Traction [OR] 4001.)			
Bamberger RR (UT) 400	Niles, 1910	Baldwin 79-33AT	DE DT Control trailer
(Originally Salt Lake & Ogden 403, then Bamberger Electric RR 320.)			
PE 457	ACF, 1911	–	DE DT "Blimp" interurban coach (body only)

(Originally Southern Pacific [Oakland, Alameda & Berkeley lines] 332, then Interurban Electric Railway 332, requisitioned by U.S. Maritime Commission in 1942, sent to PE as 332, bought by PE 1947 as 4637, became 457 in 1947, LAMTA 1707 in 1958.)

B. Interurban and Electric Freight Cars, *continued*

Salt Lake & Utah 751   Niles, 1916   Baldwin 79-35AT   DE DT Parlor obsvtn control trailer

Oregon Electric 1001   Niles, 1910   Baldwin 79-30AT   DE DT Parlor obsvtn. "Champoeg."

Sacramento Northern 1005   Holman, 1912   Baldwin 79-30B   DE DT Combine
(Originally Oakland, Antioch & Eastern, later Key System [CA] 495.)

Sacramento Northern 1019, 1020   Hall Scott, 1913   Baldwin 79—30B   DE DT Trailer
(1019 originally Oakland, Antioch & Eastern car, later maintenance of way car. 1020 is a control trailer.)

Sacramento Northern   Niles, 1906   Baldwin 79-30AT   DE DT Parlor obsvtn. "Bidwell"

C. Rapid Transit Cars

New York, Manhattan Ry. 844, 889   Gilbert, 1887   Alco/Gilbert   DE DT Elevated car
(Originally trailer cars, later IRT 844, 889, became Richmond [CA] Shipyard Ry. 561, 563 in 1942.)

D. Work Cars and Locomotives

San Francisco MUNI 0109   Hammond, 1900   Peckham 9A   DE ST Rail grinder
(Was URR Dump car 0109 from 1912, later became Market Street Ry. rail grinder 0109.)

San Francisco MUNI 0130   Home-built, 1907   Peckham 14B3S   DE DT crane

Sacramento Northern 602   Holman, 1911   Baldwin B79-30B   DE DT bunk car
(Originally Oakland, Antioch & Eastern 102)

Sacramento Nthn. 652, 654   Alco/GE 1930   GE 105A   DE DT Steeple-cab locomotive

Oakland, East Bay Traction 1011   Home-built, 1906   St. Louis MCB 23   DE DT Wrecker

Key System (CA) 1014   Hammond, 1897   –   DE DT Wrecker (body only)
(Originally Piedmont & Mtn. View Electric Ry. 140, later San Francisco-Oakland Terminal Ry. 228.)

Key System (CA) 1201   Carter Bros. 1895   Brill 27-A   DE DT Line car
(Originally California Ry. 21, later San Francisco Oakland Terminal Railway car.)

Key System (CA) 1215   Oakland Tmnl. 1899, rebuilt Gilbert 1926   Unknown   DE ST Shop Switcher

Key System (CA) 1218   Oakland Tmnl. 1929   Unknown   DE DT Flat car

E. Motor Buses

MOTOR BUSES	BUILDER AND DATE	SERIAL NUMBER
Key System (CA) 1921	GM TDH-4509, 1949	048 (Diesel)
Key System (CA) 2103	GM TDH-4801, 1958	530 (Diesel)

San Anselmo

Pacific Bus Museum, *PO Box 91, San Anselmo CA 94979-0091. (415) 256-8161. Bus museum, not yet open to the public.*

The PBM began in 1989 and was incorporated in 1991. It preserves bus history, collects, restores and operates historic buses. Members and their guests use the historic fleet for field trips which typically trace the history and routes of a transit company. Buses can also be chartered to attend gatherings or events where they can be viewed by the public. The collection as yet has no permanent home: fundraising activities are now focused on acquiring a permanent facility somewhere in northern California.

BUS	BUILDER AND DATE	SERIAL NUMBER
Modesto Motor Bus 118	GM TDH-3501, 1967	1043 (Diesel)
Sacramento TA 128	GM TDH-4512, 1958	2807 (Diesel)
Las Vegas-Reno-Tonopah Stages 172	GM PD-4106, 1964	2810 (Diesel)
Peerless Stages (CA) 246	GM TDM-4512, 1955	126 (Diesel)
Tacoma (WA) Transit 271	Twin Coach Model 41S, 1948	1167B (Gasoline)
Oklahoma TC 290	GM PD-4102, 1950	053 (Diesel)
Oakland (CA) Guiton Charter 300	GM PD-3751, 1948	714 (Diesel)
(Originally Southeastern Greyhound bus.)		
Key System (CA) 308	Twin Coach Model 15, 1932	60022 (Gasoline)
Torrance (CA) Transit 341	GM TDH-4519, 1964	285 (Diesel)
Key System (CA) 400	Twin Coach Model 30, 1933	25378 (Gasoline)
Napa Charter (CA) 518	Yellow Coach TD-4505, 1942	– (Diesel)
(Originally United States Navy bus, operated by Greyhound.)		
Virginia Stage Line 705	ACF/Brill IC-41, 1945	036 (Gasoline)

Orange County (CA) TD 1126	Flxible 53102-8-1, 1976	61187 (Diesel)
Pacific Greyhound K1407	GM TDM-5103, 1951	008 (Diesel)
Sunline 1439	Flxible 35096-6-1, 1977	62439 (Diesel)
Missouri Pacific RR 1945	GM PD-3302, 1945	016 (Diesel)
PE 2857	GM TDH-5103, 1951	559 (Diesel)
(Later Antelope Valley [CA] bus.)		
San Francisco MUNI 3270	GM T8H-5305, 1970	332 (Diesel)
Long Beach (CA) 7007	Twin Coach Model 41G, 1943	39989 (Gasoline)
(Originally Long Beach, Lang Motor Bus 749.)		
Los Angeles SCRTD 7103	Flxible 111-CC-C3-1, 1971	54895 (Diesel)
Western Greyhound 9706	GM TDH-5301, 1961	2203 (Diesel)
Glacier National Park	Flxible 29BR, 1955	30839 (Gasoline)

San Francisco

1. **Municipal Railway,** *949 Presidio Avenue, San Francisco, CA 94115. (415) 923-6212. Standard-gauge light rail, heritage and vintage trolleys, 3'6" gauge cable cars, ETBs. Heritage and vintage cars run daily on "F" line. Cable cars run daily.*

San Francisco's MUNI opened its first car line in 1912 in a city dominated by private transit companies. In 1944 MUNI bought its last major competitor and achieved a near-monopoly over the city's mass transit when it bought the California Street Cable RR Co. in 1952. On September 1, 1995 MUNI started heritage trolley service on the new "F" line between Transbay Terminal and Castro via Market Street. Originally Melbourne cars were to be used but a late-1980s export embargo led MUNI to consider using their own PCCs, stored since replaced by light rail cars in 1981. Costs, however, were prohibitive when compared with refurbishing Philadelphia PCCs which became available in 1992 and only a few MUNI cars will be done. PCC cars run on the "F" Market Street line, each in a different color scheme as a salute to North America's PCC-operators. Ridership has exceeded all expectations and many are deserting the MUNI-Metro subway to ride on the surface of Market Street.

A. City and Suburban Cars

CAR	BUILDER AND DATE	TRUCKS	CAR TYPE
Vera Cruz (Mexico) 001	Unknown	Brill 21-E	DE DT 9-bench open
San Francisco MUNI 1	Holman, 1912	Brill 27-G	DE DT Type A city
Orel (Russia) 106	Unknown, built circa 1921	Unknown radial axle	DE ST City
(Originally a Moscow car, transferred to Orel in 1960, became an Orel work car in 1978.)			
San Francisco MUNI 130	Jewett, 1914	Baldwin	DE DT Type B city
Oporto (Portugal) CCFP 189	Home-built, 1926	Brill 21-E	DE DT Semi-convertible
Blackpool Corporation (England) 228	English Electric, 1934	English Electric 4'	DE DT Open "Boat" car
(Renumbered 603 in 1968.)			
Johnstown (PA) TC 557	St. Louis, 1926	St. Louis EDJ-64	DE DT Lightweight city
Melbourne (Australia) M&MTB 496	James Moore, 1928	Melbourne Type 1	DE DT Type W2 drop-center city
Hiroshima Electric Ry. (Japan) 578J	Fujinagata Zosen, 1927	Brill 77-E	DE DT Type K city
(Originally Kobe (Japan) 574, became 578 in 1958, Hiroshima 578 in 1971. Possibly rebuilt 1959 by Sharyo Kogo of Osaka.)			
San Francisco MSR 578S	Hammond, 1896	Peckham 8	DE ST "California"
(Was URR/MSR/MUNI sand car 0601 from 1907 until restored by MUNI in 1956.)			
Melbourne (Australia) M&MTB 586	Home-built, 1929	Melbourne type 1	DE DT Type W2 drop-center city
San Francisco MSR 798	Home-built, 1924	Melbourne type 1	DE DT City
Milan (Italy) 1834	Officine Elettro-ferroviarie Tallero, 1928	ATM Milano	SE DT "Peter Witt" city
Hamburg (Germany) 3557	Linke-Hoffman-Busch, 1951	Unknown	DE DT Type V6E city

Toronto TTC Type A-7 MU PCC cars 4404, 4472 and 4481 were bought by the Market Street Railway in 1990, but later resold to Gunnar Henrioulle at Lake Tahoe.

B. PCC Cars for F-Line Heritage Service

(Cars 1050-1063's original Philadelphia numbers follow present MUNI numbers)

| San Francisco MUNI | St. Louis, 1948 | St. Louis B-3 | DE DT Type D PCC |

1006, 1007, 1008, 1010, 1014, 1015 (MUNI 1948 grn.)
(1006 in MUNI 1948 green, 1007 in 1996 MUNI colors. 1008 a repair car 1978-1996, 1010 in MUNI 1939 blue/yellow, 1015 in Illinois Terminal RR green.)

San Francisco MUNI 1040	St. Louis, 1951	St. Louis B-3	SE DT PCC (MUNI 1952 green)
San Francisco MUNI 1050 (2119)	St. Louis, 1948	Clark B-2	SE DT PCC (MUNI 1947 green)
San Francisco MUNI 1051 (2123)	St. Louis, 1948	Clark B-2	SE DT PCC (MUNI 1964 green)
San Francisco MUNI 1052 (2110)	St. Louis, 1948	Clark B-2	SE DT PCC (LA Ry. orange/yellow)
San Francisco MUNI 1053 (2721)	St. Louis, 1947	Clark B-2	SE DT PCC (Brooklyn silver/green)
San Francisco MUNI 054 (2121)	St. Louis, 1947	Clark B-2	SE DT PCC (Phila. 1938 silver)
San Francisco MUNI 1055 (2122)	St. Louis, 1948	Clark B-2	SE DT PCC (Philadelphia PTC green)
San Francisco MUNI 1056 (2113)	St. Louis, 1948	Clark B-2	SE DT PCC (Kansas City cream/black)
San Francisco MUNI 1057 (2138)	St. Louis, 1948	Clark B-2	SE DT PCC (Cincinnati yellow)
San Francisco MUNI 1058 (2124)	St. Louis, 1948	Clark B-2	SE DT PCC (Chicago CTA green)
San Francisco MUNI 1059 (2099)	St. Louis, 1948	Clark B-2	SE DT PCC (Boston MTA orange)
San Francisco MUNI 1060 (2715)	St. Louis, 1947	Clark B-2	SE DT PCC (Newark TNJ 1954 gray)
San Francisco MUNI 1061 (2116)	St. Louis, 1948	Clark B-2	SE DT PCC (Pacific Electric red)
San Francisco MUNI 1062 (2101)	St. Louis, 1948	Clark B-2	SE DT PCC (Louisville green)
San Francisco MUNI 1063 (2096)	St. Louis, 1948	Clark B-2	SE DT PCC (Baltimore yellow)
San Francisco MUNI 1064 (2133)	St. Louis, 1048	Clark B-2	SE DT PCC (MUNI 1912 red/gray)

(This car is being made handicapped-accessible.)

St. Louis PS 1704	St. Louis, 1946	Clark B-2	SE DT PCC (St. Louis PS red)

(later MUNI 1128)

Cars 1006/08/09/11/64 are still being refurbished.

C. Interurban Cars

Milan (Italy) 96	Metallica, 1931	Brill 77-E	DE DT Interurban coach
Osaka (Japan) Hankai 151	Kawasaki, 1927	Unknown	DE DT Interurban coach

D. Work Cars and Locomotives

San Francisco MUNI C-1	Pacific Car & Eqpmnt., 1923	Brill 27-MCB-2	DE DT Motor flat
San Francisco MUNI 0304	Hammond, 1900	Unknown	DE DT Line car

(Originally a San Francisco & San Mateo passenger car, became a work car in 1907.)

E. Cable Cars

There are three lines, two based on Powell Street, one on California Street. Increased tourist ridership generated by F-line car service has property owners in the Castro neighborhood talking of restoring the former Castro Street cable car line. Running on Castro between 18th and 26th Streets, the line was abandoned in 1941. Talk is of a route from 17th and Market (the F-line terminal) to 24th Street and Castro linking two commercial and retail districts. An early-1970s plan to extend the Powell-Fisherman's Wharf Line four blocks north to Pier 45, was recently dusted off, but the estimated $22 million cost has yet to be funded.

I. Powell Street

Cars are single-end, single grip, half-open, half-closed. Present numbering dates from 1973.

1		Home-built, 1973 but has roof and other small parts of 506 (I)
2 *(Originally 502)*	Carter, 1891	Rebuilt by MUNI 1971
3 *(Originally 503)*	Carter, 1891	Rebuilt by MUNI 1955
4 (II)	Home-built, 1993	Replaced 4 (I) (formerly 504, originally 543.)

(4 [I] built in 1887 by Mahoney Bros. of San Francisco for the Ferries & Cliff House Ry., was retired in September 1993. It will be restored to original condition as open car 543 by the Market Street Railway Co.)

I. Powell Street, *continued*

5	*(Originally 505)*	Carter, 1891	Rebuilt by MUNI 1956
6	*(Formerly 506 [II], originally 518)*	Carter, 1891	
7	*(Originally 507)*	Carter, 1891	Rebuilt by MUNI 1957
8	*(Originally 508)*	Carter, 1891	Rebuilt by MUNI 1958
9	*(Formerly 509, originally 542)*	Mahoney, 1887	Rebuilt by MUNI 1952
10	*(Originally 510)*	Carter, 1891	Rebuilt by MUNI 1960
11	*(Originally 511)*	Carter, 1891	Rebuilt by MUNI 1980
12	*(Originally 512)*	Carter, 1891	Rebuilt by MUNI 1959
13	*(II)*	Home-built, 1992	Replaced 13 (I) (originally 513.)
14	*(Formerly 514, originally 529)*	Carter, 1891	Rebuilt by MUNI 1963
15	*(Originally 515)*	Carter, 1891	Rebuilt by MUNI 1954
16	(I) *(Originally 516)*	Carter, 1891	Rebuilt by MUNI 1953
16	*(II)*	Home-built, 1991	Replaced 16 (I)
17	*(Formerly 517, originally 532)*	Mahoney, 1887	Rebuilt by MUNI 1956
18	*(Formerly 518 [II])*	Home-built, 1962 but has roof and other small parts of 518 (I)	
19	*(Formerly 500, originally 519)*	Carter, 1891	
20	*(Originally 520)*	Carter, 1891	Rebuilt by MUNI 1967
21	*(II)*	Home-built, 1982	Replaced 21 (I) (formerly 521, originally 533.)
22	*(Originally 522)*	Mahoney, 1887	Rebuilt by MUNI 1956
23	*(Originally 523)*	Ferries & Cliff House Ry. 1890	Rebuilt by MUNI 1969
24	*(Formerly 524, originally 534)*	Mahoney, 1887	Rebuilt by MUNI 1958
25	*(Originally 525)*	Ferries & Cliff House Ry. 1890	Rebuilt by MUNI 1976
26	*(Originally 526)*	Ferries & Cliff House Ry. 1890	Rebuilt by MUNI 1975
27	*(Originally 527)*	Mahoney, 1887	Rebuilt by MUNI 1958
28	*(Formerly 501, originally 544)*	Mahoney, 1887	Rebuilt by MUNI 1952

II. California Street

All are double-end double-grip "California" cars.

42	(O'Farrell, Jones & Hyde car.)	Holman, 1906
	(Sold in 1955, this car was re-acquired in 1995 and restored to 1920s condition.)	
49	(III)	Home-built 1992
	(Replaced 49 [II], formerly 6 [II], originally 40, built by California Cable in 1910.)	
50		Cal. Cable, 1910
51		Holman, 1906
52	(III)	Home-built, 1995
	(Replaced 52 II [formerly 3 II, originally 18] Hammond, 1907, which replaced 52 [I] sold out of service in 1954. 52 (II) was scrapped circa 1984.)	
53		Holman, 1907
54	(Originally 19.)	Hammond, 1907
55	(Originally 8.)	Hammond, 1906
56		Cal. Cable, 1913
57, 58		Cal. Cable, 1914
59	(Originally 15.)	Hammond, 1907
60	(Originally 16.)	Hammond, 1907	Rebuilt by MUNI 1969

Several cars were sold to Knott's Berry Farm (Los Angeles) in 1954 and converted to battery-electric operation to move visitors from the parking lots to the main entrance. They were out of use by the 1970s. Cars 6 [1], 20, 49 [1] and 59 [1]) were returned to MUNI in 1981. Worn-out bodies and electrolyte damage made them too costly to restore and they were auctioned on December 10, 1994. Jones Street shuttle 62 (II), (originally 61) is now a motorized rubber-tired display vehicle. Others sold in the 1950s and 1960s to Gridley Realty (including 1, 3, 7, 11, 12, 52 [1], 60), were also converted and sometimes run in the city. The venture has no connection with MUNI. Gridley may also own Sacramento-Clay cable cars 18 and 25. The original 61 was donated to Osaka (Japan) at an unknown date. Sacramento-Clay 19 is stored by the Market Street Ry. for future restoration.

F. Electric Trolley Buses

BUS	BUILDER AND DATE	SERIAL NUMBER
San Francisco, MSR 50	Twin Coach 41GWFT, 1940	75170
(Recreation of Brill original, made from Seattle 836, later 614.)		
Philadelphia SEPTA 325	Marmon-Herrington TC49, 1955	15501
San Francisco MUNI 506	St. Louis, 1939	–

Dayton (OH) CTC/Miami Valley RTA 559	Marmon-Herrington TC48, 1948	10486
(Originally Columbus & Southern Ohio Electric 643, Became Dayton 559 in 1965, painted as Christmas coach in 1978.)		
San Francisco MUNI 776	Marmon-Herrington TC48, 1950	10867
San Francisco MUNI 5001/02	Western Flyer E-700A, 1971/1973	1271149, 0273269

G. Motor Buses

San Francisco MUNI 062 (originally 042)	White 784, 1938	209476 (Gasoline)
San Francisco MUNI 0105/09	White 798, 1945, 1946	302818, 302372 (Gasoline)
San Francisco MUNI 0163/65	Twin Coach 44D, 1947	147, 149 (Gasoline)
(0163 on loan from Orange Empire Railway Museum.)		
San Francisco MUNI 0419 (body only), 0425	White 798, 1948	358923 (0425)
San Francisco MUNI 2246	Mack C49 DT, 1956	1300 (Diesel)
San Francisco MUNI 3287	GM T8H-5305, 1969	349 (Diesel)
San Francisco MUNI 4009	Flxible 111-CC-C3, 1969	54044 (Diesel)
San Francisco MUNI 4154	AM General 9635-6, 1975	390 (Diesel)

2. Market Street Ry. Co., *PO Box 425063, San Francisco, CA 94142-5063. (415) 863-1775.*

The MSR Company (named for the private transit company bought by MUNI in 1944) was set up in 1985 to restore cars of MUNI's Historic Trolley Festival (see below), promote historic car use on Market Street and support regular operation of MUNI's historic transit fleet in charters and historic parades. It originated in the late 1970s when several people, including local travel agent Maurice H. Klebolt, saved a MUNI ETB from the scrapyard. With that task accomplished and with MUNI Metro's 1981 opening imminent, Klebolt bought a car from Hamburg, displayed it and then donated it to MUNI.

The cable cars were absent between 1982 and 1984 when reconstruction (the first since they were built) consumed their tracks. Tourist dollars were threatened and the Chamber of Commerce suggested using Market Street trackage (disused since September 19, 1981) for an historic trolley festival, a tourist-friendly alternative to the cable cars. There was a precedent for this in MUNI's mini-heritage trolley service promoting the proposed E-Embarcadero waterfront tourist line in 1981. The proposal was agreed and the trolley festival began June 22, 1983. It was a massive hit. Klebolt and the MSR were among its most enthusiastic backers, lobbying successfully for MUNI to acquire more cars to make the "trolleyfest" as famous as the cable cars.

With the old trolleys' popularity proven, the city now sought funding for a new F-Market line using old cars on Market Street tracks, plus an extension to Fisherman's Wharf on the proposed E-Embarcadero route. The MSR was of material assistance in seeing these projects mature and despite Klebolt's untimely death in 1988, it continues to acquire and restore old cars to donate to the city. MSR's "Museum in Motion" program places interpretive photo displays and memorabilia inside the vehicles. Through its affiliation with Local Independent Charities, MSR is a part of several major Bay Area charitable programs, including the United Way.

3. San Francisco Cable Car Museum, *1201 Mason Street, San Francisco, CA 94108. (415) 474-1887. Open daily 10:00 a.m.-5:00 p.m.*

The creation of the San Francisco Cable Car Museum in the cable car barn and powerhouse at Washington & Mason was a direct consequence of MUNI's surviving cable car lines being designated a National Historical landmark in 1964. The first cable grip car of 1873 (Clay Street Hill RR 8) is displayed together with grip dummy 46 and trailer 54 of the Sutter Street Ry. Co. (both built in 1879). Many other smaller artifacts are on display in the still-functioning cable powerhouse.

San Jose

1. Kelley Park Trolley. California Trolley & Railroad Corporation, *PO Box 403, Campbell, CA 95009. Standard-gauge tourist trolley. Cars run weekends year-round noon-4:00 p.m in Kelley Park, 1600 Senter Road, San Jose, CA 95112. (408) 293-2276.*

Kelley Park is a 16-acre open air city museum. Its focal point is a plaza around which are grouped authentic 19th century homes, businesses and hotels, transplanted from their original sites and linked by a working trolley line. The custom-built trolley shop and barn replicates a typical 19th-century installation and is itself a park exhibit. This shop restored the park trolley and (for the San Jose Trolley Corporation) the historic cars running on San Jose's light rail line. The park line originally was a test track for these cars. Only later was it lengthened and integrated into the park as a fully developed exhibit. The first park car ran on April 11, 1988 and the tracks are shortly to be extended to Happy Hollow Park.

San Jose's Lenzen Street roundhouse, the last operational railroad roundhouse in California, was damaged in the 1989 Loma Prieta earthquake. The Southern Pacific RR was ready to tear it down but the Santa Clara Valley RR Association and others were able to get it listed as an historic structure and persuaded the SP to donate it to Santa Clara County. It is being re-erected at the county fairgrounds as the centerpiece of a new museum based on the SCVRRA's railroad collection. A replica of San Jose's original Southern Pacific depot will be built to serve as a vehicle display area and the county archives.

The presence of two locally-focused rail museum facilities within a mile of each other led to thoughts of union and in November 1994, San Jose Trolley Corporation and the SCVRRA merged to become the California Trolley and Railroad Corporation. The CTRC in 1995 was the recipient of an ISTEA grant to build a one-mile trolley line on existing spur tracks to link Kelley Park and the Santa Clara County fairgrounds. It is scheduled to open in 1998.

A. City and Suburban Cars

CARS	BUILDER AND DATE	TRUCKS	CAR TYPE
San Francisco, Central RR Co. 7	Stephenson, 1863	Pedestal	DE ST Horse car
(Originally numbered 15, then 7 and later numbered 11.)			
Fresno Traction Co. 68	American, 1920	Unknown	DE ST Birney "safety"
San Jose RR 129	American, 1913	Brill 27-G	DE DT "California"
(Originally Sacramento, Pacific Gas & Electric 35. On loan from Santa Clara County Transportation District.)			
San Jose RR 143	St. Louis, 1920	Brill 79-E-1	DE ST Birney "safety"
(Originally Fresno (CA) Traction 68.)			
San Jose RR 168	CCFP, 1936	Brill 21-E	DE ST Semi-convertible
(Originally Oporto [Portugal] CCFP 154 [II], became 174 in 1985 just before it was shipped to San Jose.)			

Melbourne (Australia) W2 403 (home-built, 1926) and Milan (Italy) "Peter Witt" 1941 (Officine Elettro Ferroviarie Tallero, 1929) were acquired for parts.

2. **Valley Transportation Authority,** *3331 N. First Street, San Jose, CA 95134. (408) 299-8600. Tourist trolleys run on the standard-gauge light rail line daily between Memorial Day and Labor Day, otherwise weekends year-round.*

Tourist trolleys on downtown segments of San Jose's light rail line were planned from the beginning. The San Jose Trolley Corporation was set up in 1982 to fund and direct the restoration of six vintage cars for this purpose. Restoration began in 1984 at the Kelley Park trolley shop under the supervision of Fred Bennett, formerly of Connecticut's Shore Line Museum. Compromises with historical authenticity give collision-damage protection to the cars. Thus, these are not museum restorations but refurbishments approximating those a latter-day San Jose transit operator would have done had the cars survived in service to the 1990s. All were once bodies without trucks or motors. Melbourne or Milan equipment, new steel underframes, reinforced collision fenders and other parts have been used to get them back on the road. Most are restricted to street-running segments, but the Milan car has covered the whole light rail system in charter operation.

A. City and Suburban Cars

CARS	BUILDER AND DATE	TRUCKS	CAR TYPE
Santa Clara Interurban RR 1	Pacific Gas & Electric, 1906	ATM Milano	DE DT "California" with convertible center section
(Originally Sacramento, Pacific Gas & Electric 9, then Union Traction Co. of Santa Cruz No. 1 in 1906.)			
San Jose RR 73	Jewett, 1912	Melbourne Type 1	DE DT "California"
(Originally San Jose RR 130, later Peninsular Railways 73.)			
San Jose RR 124	American, 1912	Brill 27-G	DE DT "California"
Melbourne (Australia) M&MTB 531	Home-built, 1928	Melbourne Type 1B	DE DT Type W2 drop-center city
Milan (Italy) 2001	O. M. Lodigiane, 1929	ATM Milano	DE DT City
(Originally a single-end "Peter Witt" car, it was damaged in a 1943 air-raid and subsequently cannibalized for parts. To San Jose in 1986, rebuilt to double-end by San Jose Trolley Corpn. at Kelley Park using parts from accident-damaged Milan 1941.)			

COLORADO

Aspen

Aspen Street Ry. Company, 548 Race Street, Aspen, CO. 81611. (970) 925-6431. Proposed 2' 11 7/16" gauge tourist trolley.

This would have been one of America's earliest new-start stand-alone tourist trolleys had it been completed within a year or so of acquiring its six Lisbon cars in the 1970s. A new mayor and a change of political climate stopped the project cold and the cars languished outdoors (protected by covers) for nearly twenty years. Recently the plan was dusted off as an alternative to a cross-town bus shuttle. A mile of track will run from South Galena Street at Dean (the base of Aspen Mountain and terminal of gondola and chairlift #1), north on Galena through downtown and around the east and north sides of the Rio Grande playing fields, ending at the Post Office shopping center, using four cars. Aspen has set up an IRS 6320 corporation to implement the project, a device allowing a city to create a non-profit entity to start a "public good" project and raise money for it by issuing bonds. When the line is complete, the city will take over from the corporation via the Roaring Fork Transit Agency (the present bus operator) who will run it. A project manager was hired and a final review was made in spring, 1996.

A second project being discussed is an alternative to a state-proposed four-lane highway entrance to Aspen. The city would prefer light rail in place of (or at least as part of) the new highway, to reduce the number of autos entering town. An alternative could be vintage light rail using standard-gauge cars. The ASR is developing such a plan for the city. A 1/2 cent sales tax increase was recently passed, dedicated specifically for the alternative entrance project and this would finance construction of the light rail line and vehicle purchase. Mixed gauge operation (vintage light rail and Lisbon tourist cars) on downtown streets would be a possibility. The cars are Lisbon 418 [St. Louis, 1900], 519-521, 524, 526 [home-built, 1925]. One car is lettered "Aspen Street Railway Company 23, Galena Street").

Colorado Springs

Pikes Peak Historical Street Railway Foundation, PO Box 544, Colorado Springs, CO 80901. (719) 475-9508. Operates standard-gauge Colorado Springs & Interurban Ry. Co. tourist trolley. Carhouse at 2333 Steel Drive. Open Saturdays year round.

The PPHSRF was set up in 1982 to reactivate part of the old Colorado Springs street railway "to . . .improve mobility, generate economic development and tourism and help . . . restore an important element of (city) history." The CSIRC is the PPHSRF's operational arm and will restore $1^1/_2$ miles on West Colorado Avenue (last used in 1932) from Tejon Street downtown to 28th Street in Old Colorado City. The first wires were erected on 200 yards of former railroad trackage around the carhouse (a one-time Chicago, Rock Island & Pacific RR locomotive shed) and test runs began November 29, 1995 with car 2129 in the dark green and gold colors of the old Colorado Springs and Interurban Railway. The carhouse interpretive center opened July 4, 1996, when 2129 began regular runs. All the PCCs have corporate sponsors, 2131 being the "Sky Sox" car of the Colorado Springs Sky Sox baseball team. It is displayed at Sky Sox Stadium. The team's owner is a former Philadelphian and at his request, 2131 is now in its original Philadelphia PTC colors. It will stay at the stadium until needed for service.

Kimley Horn & Associates, a transportation planning and engineering firm (with 500 full-time staff in 28 cities) has developed special expertise in vintage street railway planning and implementation. The firm recently completed a study for Colorado Springs suggesting that 16.6 miles of track should ultimately be built on five separate routes serving North Tejon Street, Colorado College, Old Colorado City and Manitou Springs. The lines would use as much as possible of the CS&IR's original routes.

CAR	BUILDER AND DATE	TRUCKS	CAR TYPE
Fort Collins MUNI 22	American, 1919	Brill 78-M-1-F	DE ST Birney "safety"
(Leased from Rocky Mtn. RR. Club. Being restored as Colorado Springs & Manitou 135, following on from the old streetcar number series.)			
Colorado Springs and Interurban 59	Laclede, 1901	–	DE ST City Car (body only)
Philadelphia SEPTA 2093/97/102/07/09/14/29/31/2722	St. Louis, 1948 (2722, 1947)	St. Louis B-3	SE DT PCC
(All wide-gauge Philadelphia Clark B-2 trucks replaced by standard-gauge ex-Chicago trucks.)			

25

Denver

1. Old Spaghetti Factory Restaurant, *1215 18th Street, Denver, CO 80202. (303) 295-1864.*

The Old Spaghetti Factory restaurant has the body of Woeber-built Denver Tramways 54 as its dining-room centerpiece.

2. Platte Valley Trolley, *2200 Seventh Street, Denver, CO. 80211-5215. (303) 458-6255. Standard-gauge tourist trolley, owned and operated by Denver Rail Heritage Society. Car runs daily in summer (except on those Mondays when the Children's Museum is closed) 11:00 a.m.-3:00 p.m. Longer hours at weekends. Weekend only operation in winter.*

The DRHS preserves Maffat Road station, operates the PVT along the bank of the Platte River, and collects other rail artifacts. The trolley boards at the Children's Museum near Decatur Street and runs north along the west bank of the Platte River to the Forney Museum at Fifteenth Street and Confluence Park. A once-a-day extension runs from the Children's Museum to Lakewood between April and October, on part of the former Denver Tramways Golden interurban line, closed in 1950. The trolley line is unwired and the car is powered from its on-board generator. Service began in the early 1990s.

A. City and Suburban Cars

CAR	BUILDER AND DATE	TRUCKS	CAR TYPE
Gomaco 1977	Gomaco, 1984	Melbourne Type 1	DE DT 15-bench Brill replica open
(This car is leased from GOMACO.)			
*Denver & Intermountain RR 25	Woeber, 1911	Mcguire-Cummings	DE DT Suburban
(This car, owned by the Rocky Mountain RR Club, PO Box 2391, Denver CO. 80201, is being restored at the Denver Federal Center in cooperation with the Rocky Mountain RR Historical Foundation and the Denver Rail Heritage Society.)			

Denver RTD owns Denver Tramways 117 (Woeber, 1914, body only) which is used as a light rail station shelter, plus Denver Tramways buses 119 (GM TDH-5105, 1958, serial 3369) and 132 (Mack C47 DT, 1959 serial 1436).The Forney museum has a Denver cable car body.

Fort Collins

Fort Collins Municipal Railway Society, *PO Box 635, Fort Collins, CO 80522. (970) 224-5372. Standard-gauge tourist trolley. Operates weekends and holidays April-September, noon-5:00 p.m.*

The FCMRS has revived Fort Collins trolley operation (absent from the town since 1951) on original right-of-way along Mountain and Roosevelt Avenues to City Park, using Fort Collins MUNI 21 (American, 1919, Brill 78-M-1-F) a Birney "safety" car, which since 1951 had languished on static display in City Park. This one car has run all summer and early fall services ever since the first public run on December 29, 1984. A railroad grade crossing prevents through service to a revived cultural and tourist area, but it is within a short walk of the trolley.

Pueblo

Steel Town Trolleys, *Pueblo Union Depot, 132 West "B" Street, Pueblo, CO 81003. Proposed standard-gauge tourist trolley.*

For years a Birney "safety" car operator, Southern Colorado Power Company ran its last Pueblo car on November 29, 1947. The STT (aka Pueblo Street Railway Foundation) lobbies for community support and assistance in getting trolleys back onto city streets. Present thinking envisages a one-mile tourist line from Union Depot to serve a new hotel and convention center on First Street. A 1995 voter-approved downtown redevelopment project included a tourist trolley line, but funding is currently only available for design work. Two Pueblo Birney bodies were recently bought from Maurine Clevinger after decades on her family ranch. One is Arkansas Valley Railway Light & Power (the pre-1923 Pueblo trolley operator) 84 (American, 1923). Two Brussels (Belgium) NMVB/STIB cars, (motor 1245, home-Built, 1937, trailer 2190, AM de Nivelles, 1931, [later 1611 and 607]) were bought in 1996 from Orlando's Grand Cypress resort. A Brussels PCC is also to be bought.

CONNECTICUT

East Haven

Shore Line Trolley Museum, 17 River Street, East Haven, CT 06512-2519. (203) 467-6927. Standard-gauge trolley museum. Cars run 11:00 a.m.-5:00 p.m. daily Memorial Day-Labor Day, weekends May, September and October, Sundays in April, November.

Established in August 1945 as the Branford Electric Railway Association, this was the first trolley museum to acquire a home on a still-operating route, the Connecticut Company's historic Shore Line, an immensely scenic 1 1/2 mile run through tidewater creeks and salt marshes. Irregular public runs began in 1949, regularly scheduled runs in 1953. Several cars are native to New Haven and at least one car is native to the very line the museum now owns. This strong regional collection specializes in southern New England, New York City and mid-Atlantic Seaboard vehicles. The museum is part of a neighborhood coalition which has successfully raised money to buy surrounding lands and so prevent encroachment by developers on this unique shoreline environment.

A. City and Suburban Cars

CAR	BUILDER AND DATE	TRUCKS	CAR TYPE
New York, Metropolitan St. Ry. 3	Stephenson, 1893	Pedestal	DE ST Horse car
Philadelphia SEPTA (Red Arrow) 8	Brill, 1941	Brill 89-E-2	DE DT "Brilliner" suburban
Toronto TTC 11	TTC, 1933	Pedestal	DE ST Replica 1890s horse car
Philadelphia SEPTA (Red Arrow) 18/21	St. Louis, 1949	St. Louis	DE DT Suburban MU PCC
Lynchburg (VA) Ry. 34	Jackson & Sharp, 1899	Brill 21-E	DE ST 9-bench open
(Later owned by Five Mile Beach (Wildwood NJ) Electric Ry.)			
Providence, Rhode Island Co. 61	Jones, 1893	Bemis 26	DE DT City
Goteborg (Sweden) Sparvagar 71	ASEA, 1912	ASEA	DE ST City
Philadelphia SEPTA (Red Arrow) 84	Brill, 1933	Brill 89-E-1	DE DT Lightweight suburban
Staten Island Midland RR 157	St. Louis, 1895	–	DE ST City (body only)
(Acquired 1996 from the Old Richmondtown Historic site in Staten Island.)			
Consolidated (CT.) 193	Jewett, 1904	Standard 0-50	DE DT City/suburban
(Later Connecticut Co. 775.)			
New York, Metropolitan St. Ry. 220	Laclede, 1892	Peckham 11	DE ST City, originally cable
New York, Union Ry. 316	American, 1895	Peckham 8-B	DE ST City
Johnstown (PA) Transit Co. 356/7	St. Louis, 1926	St. Louis EDJ-64	DE DT Lightweight city
Consolidated (CT) 401	Jones, 1906	Taylor SB	DE DT 15-bench open
(Later Connecticut Co. 923.)			
Connecticut Co. 500	Brill, 1904	Brill 27-E-1	DE DT Parlor
Consolidated (CT) 614	Brill, 1901	Brill 27-G	DE DT 15-bench open
(Later Connecticut Co. 302.)			
New York TARS 629	Home-built, 1939	Brill 39-E	DE DT Lightweight city
(Later Vienna [Austria] Stadtwerke Verkehrsbetriebe 4239.)			
Washington Ry. & Electric 650	Brill, 1912	Brill 27-G-1	DE DT Center-entrance semi-convertible
(Later Capital Transit 884.)			
New York TARS 830	Brill, 1908	Brill 39-E	DE DT City
New Orleans PSI 850	Perley Thomas, 192	Brill 76-E-2	DE DT City

A. City and Suburban Cars, *continued*

Consolidated (CT) 865	Wason, 1905	Standard 0-50	DE DT City/suburban
(Later Connecticut Co. 512. Built for the line now operated by the museum.)			
New York TARS 884	Brill, 1909	Brill 39-E	DE DT Convertible
Atlanta, Georgia Power Co. 948	Cincinnati, 1926	Brill 77-E	DE DT City
Brooklyn BQT 1001	St. Louis, 1936	Clark B-2	SE DT PCC
Connecticut Co. 1199	Stephenson, 1906	Standard 0-50	DE DT City
(Originally operated in Stamford CT. Later numbered 283.)			
Connecticut Co. 1330 (later 554)	Osgood Bradley, 1910	Standard 0-50	DE DT City
Montreal Tramways 1403	Ottawa, 1914	Brill 27-G	DE DT City
Connecticut Co. 1414/25 (later 448/59)	Osgood Bradley, 1911	Standard 0-50	DE DT 15-bench open
Connecticut Co. 1602 (later 612)	Wason, 1911	Standard 0-50	DE DT City
Toronto TTC 1706	Toronto Ry., 1913	Curtis 5896	DE ST Type E convertible
(Became TTC rail-grinder W-24 in 1925.)			
Nassau (NY) Electric Ry. 1792	Laclede, 1899	Brill 39-E	DE DT City
Connecticut Co. 1802	Wason, 1915	Standard 0-36	DE DT City
Connecticut Co. 1911	Brill, 1919	Standard C55P	DE DT Suburban
Montreal MTC 1972, 2001	CCF, 1929	CCF 177	DE DT City
Connecticut Co. 2350	Osgood Bradley, 1922	OB 25-96	DE ST Birney "safety"
Public Service of New Jersey 2431	Cincinnati, 1913	Standard C50-P	SE DT City
Toronto TTC 2898	Ottawa, 1923	CCF 3550	SE DT Type P-2 Small "Peter Witt" city
Connecticut Co. 3000	Wason, 1922	Brill 77-E-1	DE DT Birney "safety"
Brooklyn BMT 4573	Laconia, 1906	Peckham 25	DE DT Convertible
Boston ER 5706	Brill, 1924	Standard C35P	DE DT Type 5 lightweight city
Brooklyn BMT 8111	St. Louis, 1923	Brill 77-E-1	DE DT "Peter Witt" city

Boston MBTA PCC 3323 (originally Dallas Railway & Terminal 605 Pullman, 1945) has been deaccessioned.

B. Interurban Cars

Montreal & So. Co. 9	Grand Trunk Ry., 1911	Curtis C1-158-72	DE DT Interurban coach
Cincinnati & Lake Erie 116	Cincinnati, 103	Cincinnati ABC74D	DE DT Lightweight interurban coach
Monongahela West Penn 25	Jewett, 1904	Brill 27-MCB-1	DE DT Interurban coach
(Originally a Fairmont & Clarksburg Electric RR Co.car.)			
Chicago, North Shore & Milwaukee 709	Cincinnati, 1924	Baldwin 78-30A	DE DT Interurban coach

C. Rapid Transit Cars

New York Elevated RR G (later IRT)	Gilbert & Bush, 1878	Unknown	DE DT Money collection trailer car
New York Elevated RR M-8 (later IRT)	Wason, 187	Unknown	DE DT Flat car trailer
New York IRT 53 (later NYCTA 30127)	Pressed Steel, 1906	Unknown	DE DT Box tool car
New York IRT 62	Pressed Steel, 1906	ACF	DE DT Switch locomotive
New York IRT 95	Magor, 1914	Unknown	DE DT Covered hopper
New York BMT 197 (later 167, then 324)	Pullman, 1888	Unknown	DE DT Elevated passenger trailer
Staten Island RT 388	Standard, 1925	Commonwealth	DE DT Suburban RT car
Hudson & Manhattan 503	ACF, 1928	ACF	DE DT Subway
New York BMT 659	Jewett, 1901	Peckham 40	DE DT Open platform subway
Manhattan Ry. 824 (later IRT)	Pullman,, 1881	ACF	DE DT Elevated instruction
New York BMT 999	Brooklyn Hts. RR., 1905	Peckham 40	DE DT Elevated instruction
New York BMT 1227	Osgood Bradley, 1903	Peckham 40	DE DT Open platform subway
New York BMT 1349	Cincinnati, 1905	Alco 2380	DE DT Open platform convertible subway
New York BMT 1362	Jewett, 1905	Alco 2380	DE DT Open platform convertible subway
New York IND 1689	ACF, 1940	ACF Arch bar	DE DT Type R-9 subway
New York BMT 2775	Pressed Steel, 1922	A55 Arch bar	DE DT Subway

New York IRT 3344	Wason, 1904	ACF and Baldwin	DE DT Private subway car "Mineola"
New York IRT 3662	ACF, 1907	ACF and Baldwin	DE DT Subway
Chicago Elevated 4280	Cincinnati, 1922	Baldwin 78-30	DE DT Elevated
New York IRT 5466	ACF, 1924	Baldwin	DE DT Subway
New York City TA 6688	St. Louis, 1955	General Steel	DE DT Type R-17 subway

D. Work Cars and Locomotives

Abendroth Foundry "Amy"	GE, 1902	GE	DE ST Switcher
Derby Horse Ry. "Derby"	Van De Poele, 1888	Pedestal	DE ST Locomotive
Montreal MTC W-3	Differential, 1929	MTC arch-bar	DE DT Crane
South Brooklyn Ry. 4	Brooklyn Heights, 1907	Alco 2380	DE DT Locomotive
Montreal MTC 5	Peckham, 1910	Peckham 14B6	DE DT Rotary snow plow
Cornwall (ON) Street Ry. 12	Baldwin/WH, 1917	Baldwin	DT DE Steeple-cab locomotive
(Originally Utah-Idaho Central 904.)			
Ottawa OTC 25	Home-built, 1923	Taylor	DE ST Line car
Toronto TTC S-36	Russell, 1920	Brill 27-E-1	DE DT Snow sweeper
(Originally Eastern Mass. Street Railway P-607, then New York TARS 89.)			
New York TARS 59	McGuire-Cummings, 1914	McGuire-Cummings	DE ST Snow sweeper
(Originally Yonkers RR 59.)			
New Bedford (MA), Union St. Ry. 302	Jones, 1907	Standard 0-50	DE DT Mail car
Rhode Island Co. 1504	Home-built, 1904	Baldwin	DE DT Emergency car
Montreal MTC 3152	CCF, 1925	MTC arch-bar	DE DT Snow Plow
(Later Cornwall [ON] Street Railway P-8.)			
Boston MBTA 3271	St. Louis/Differential, 1920	Taylor	DE DT Dump car
Baltimore UR&E 3715 (Originally 6028.)	Home-built, 1913	Brill 27-G22	DE DT crane
Montreal MTC 5002	Home-built, 1918	CCF	DE DT Steeple-cab locomotive
New York, S. Brooklyn Ry. 9137	Middletown, 1904	Peckham 100	DE DT Rail crane
New York, S. Brooklyn Ry. 9161	Baltimore Steel, 1904	Peckham 100	DE DT Gondola car
New York, S. Brooklyn Ry. 9421, 9425	Middletown, 1903	Peckham 100	DE DT Box car
Brooklyn BQT 9799, 9800	Taunton, 1898	Taunton	DE ST Wedge plow
(9800 originally numbered 10.)			
Brooklyn BQT 9832	Brill, 1915	Brill Pedestal	DE ST Snow sweeper
Unnumbered Montreal	Home-built, 1920	Taylor	DE ST Switcher

Johnstown (PA) Transit Co. "Brick" (Home-built, 1945, ST Flat car) has been deaccessioned.

E. Electric Trolley Buses

BUS	BUILDER AND DATE	SERIAL NUMBER
Philadelphia SEPTA 205/10	ACF-Brill TC44, 1947	427/32

F. Motor Buses

Connecticut Co. 928	Yellow Coach Model 731, 1939	440 (Gasoline)
Connecticut Co. 1261	GM TDH-5105, 1957	– (Diesel)
Connecticut Co. 1491	GM TDH-5105, 1955	752 (Diesel)
Connecticut Co. 2021	GM TDH-4517, 1962	1720 (Diesel)

East Windsor

1. ***Connecticut Trolley Museum,*** *PO Box 360, East Windsor, CT 06088-0360. (860) 627-6540. Standard-gauge trolley museum, on route 140, 3/4 mile east of exit 45 on Interstate 91, north of Hartford CT. Cars run weekends year-round (except Thanksgiving and Christmas) noon- 5:00 p.m., daily Memorial Day-Labor Day 10:00 a.m.-4:00 p.m.*

The Connecticut Electric Railway Association was a 1940 spin-off from the New England Electric Railway Historical Society (North America's first trolley museum group) which had settled on a Kennebunkport ME museum site, too distant for folks south of Boston to visit regularly. The CERA thus settled here to achieve the same goals as the NEERHS: to preserve, display and operate streetcars on a demonstration track for the public. When World War II ended, the CERA created a New England trolley museum of great charm on the Hartford and Springfield Street Railway's Rockville branch roadbed, abandoned in 1926. The first car ran in April 1954, public service began in 1955. Recently, the line was extended and an ambitious new Visitors Center opened.

A. City and Suburban Cars

CAR	BUILDER AND DATE	TRUCKS	CAR TYPE
Montreal MTC 4	Home-built, 1924	Brill 27-G	SE DT Observation
Five Mile Beach (Wildwood, NJ) 36	Brill, 1895	Brill 21-E	DE ST 9-bench open
(Originally Lynchburg [VA] 36.)			
Connecticut Co. 65	Wason, 1906	Taylor SB	DE DT City
Nassau (NY) 169	St. Louis, 1894	Dupont single truck	DE ST City
Connecticut Co. 355	Brill, 1902	Brill 27-G	DE DT 15-bench open
Illinois Terminal 451	St. Louis, 1949	St. Louis B-3	DE DT MU suburban PCC
Connecticut Co. 771	Jewett, 1904	Standard 0-50	DE DT City
New Orleans PSI 836	Perley Thomas, 1922	Brill 76-E-2	DE DT City
Connecticut Co. 840	Jones, 1905	Taylor SB	DE DT 15-bench open
Shaker Heights (OH) RT 1201	Kuhlman, 1914	Brill 51-E	SE DT Center-entrance MU city
(Originally Cleveland Ry. Co. 1201.)			
Connecticut Co. 1326	Osgood Bradley, 1910	Standard 0-60	DE DT City
Rio de Janeiro (Brazil) 1850/87	Home-built, 1912	Unknown	DE DT 13-bench open
Montreal MTC 2056	Wason, 1927	Brill 177-E-1-X	SE DT Lightweight city
(Originally Springfield [MA] Ry. Co. 575.)			
Montreal MTC 2600	CCF, 1929	Unknown	DE DT Lightweight city
Connecticut Co. 3001	Wason, 1922	Brill 77-E-1	DE DT Birney "safety"
Boston MBTA 3003/100	Pullman-Standard, 1941/44	Clark B-2	SE DT MU PCC
Boston MBTA 3306/09	Pullman-Standard, 1951	Clark B-2	SE DT MU PCC
Boston MBTA 3333	Pullman-Standard, 1945	Clark B-2	SE DT MU PCC
(Originally Dallas Railway & Terminal 625.)			
Boston ER 5645	Laconia, 1923	Standard C-35P	DE DT Type 5A lightweight semi-convertible

B. Interurban and Electric Freight Cars

CAR	BUILDER AND DATE	TRUCKS	CAR TYPE
Springfield (VT) 10/16	Wason, 1901	Taylor MCB	DE DT Combine
Chicago, North Shore & Milwaukee 162	Brill, 1915	Baldwin 78-30	DE DT Interurban coach
Connecticut Co. 0206 (later 25)	Home-built, 1910	Standard 0-60	DE DT Express motor
Chicago, North Shore & Milwaukee 710	Cincinnati, 1924	Baldwin 78-30	DE DT Interurban coach
Connecticut Co. 2022	Wason, 1911	Unknown	DE DT Express motor
Connecticut Co. 2023	Home-built, 1910	Standard 0-60	DE DT Freight motor

C. Rapid Transit Cars

CAR	BUILDER AND DATE	TRUCKS	CAR TYPE
Long Island RR 4153	ACF, 1931	PRR 12D8P1/2CP3	DE DT MU MP-54A1 commuter
Chicago CTA 4175, 4284	Cincinnati, 1914/22	Baldwin 78-30	SE DT Elevated trailer
Chicago CTA 4409/36	Cincinnati, 1924	Baldwin 78-30	SE DT Elevated

E. Work Cars and Locomotives

CAR	BUILDER AND DATE	TRUCKS	CAR TYPE
Capital Transit (DC) 010	McGuire, 1899	McGuire	DE DT Snow Sweeper
Springfield VT 12	Brill 1915	Unknown	DE DT Snow plow
Auburn & Syracuse (NY) 18	Baldwin/WH, 1918	Baldwin	DE DT Locomotive
Poneman Mills S-193	Unknown	Unknown	DE ST Line car
Poneman Mills unidentified	GE, 1894	Unknown	DE ST Locomotive
Connecticut Co. 0309	Brill, 1902	Standard 0-50	DE DT Work car
Montreal MTC W-1	Home-built, 1912	Unknown	DT crane

2. Connecticut Motor Coach Museum, PO Box 297, East Windsor, CT 06088. (860) 623-4732.

The Connecticut Fire Museum (also known as the Trolley Museum Fire Department) began in 1968 and keeps its exhibits at the Connecticut Trolley Museum. Specializing in fire-fighting equipment and support vehicles, the CFM in 1986 established the CMCM as a subdivision to preserve and display antique buses of Connecticut. The buses are housed at the Connecticut Fire Museum Building and are either owned by the CMCM or leased from the state of Connecticut.

MOTOR BUSES	BUILDER AND DATE	SERIAL NUMBER
Springfield St. Ry. 169	ACF H-17-S, 1936	200 (Gasoline)
University of Ct. 207	Twin Coach TC-29	TC25142 (Diesel)
Connecticut Co. 351	Yellow Coach Model 740, 1939	289 (Diesel)
Connecticut Co. 608	Grumman 45102-6-1, 197	90277 (Diesel)
Connecticut Co. 1172	GM TDH-3610, 1948,	1476 (Diesel)
New York Bus Service 1387	GM SDM-5301, 1960	146 (Diesel)
Connecticut Co. 1488	GM TDH-5105, 1955	1288 (Diesel)
Connecticut Co. 1712	GM TDH-5304A, 1967	1951 (Diesel)
Connecticut Co. 2039	GM TDH-4517, 1962	1716 (Diesel)
Connecticut Co. 3001	GM TDH 4519A, 1965	1572 (Diesel)

DISTRICT OF COLUMBIA

Smithsonian Institution, *Supervising Curator, Division of Transportation, National Museum of American History, Washington DC 20560. Museum open daily 10:00 a.m. - 5:30 p.m.*

The Smithsonian exhibits several streetcar models built by the late William J. Clouser of St. Louis, including a model of St. Louis PS PCC car 1664. Full-size street railway exhibits include Capital Traction (DC) 303 and matching trailer 1512. The Smithsonian also owns Baltimore Coach Co. 12 (White TRC, 1917) and a US Post Office bus (White 788, 1941).

FLORIDA

Miami

Former Miami (Florida Power & Light Company) Birney "safety" 231 (Brill, 1925), owned by the City of Miami, is displayed in the local history museum next to Miami Metrorail's Government Center Station.

Tampa

Tampa and Ybor City, *c/o S. J. McGee, PO Box 5208, Tampa FL 33675. (813) 622-3912.*

The city of Tampa and the Hillborough Area RTA are proposing a $21.3 million tourist trolley line just over 2 miles long in Ybor City and have called for engineering services to begin preliminary work on the project. The line is to aid the area's economic redevelopment and reduce automobile traffic. New Birney "safety" cars (approximately) will be used. The Tampa & Ybor City Street Railway Society has restored Tampa Electric Company Birney "safety" car 163 (St. Louis, 1922) to operating condition, but it is not known whether the society and its car will have any connection with the city's project.

GEORGIA

Atlanta

(Duluth) Southeastern Railway Museum, *PO Box 1267, Duluth GA 30136-1267. (404) 476-2013.*

This railroad museum, owned by the NRHS Atlanta chapter, owns Atlanta White bus 401, Georgia Ry. & Power Co. (Atlanta) DE DT motor flat 704 (home-built 1906) and Georgia Ry. & Power (Atlanta) DE DT city car 995 (Cincinnati, 1925). It once owned New Orleans PSI 924, displayed for many years at "Underground Atlanta," but this car was sold back to New Orleans.

Shore Line Trolley Museum's Rhode Island Company car 61, seen crossing an arm of the tidal Farm River in August 1979, is one of the oldest operating streetcars in the world, having been built in 1893.

On a bright April afternoon in 1990, San Jose Railroad's 168 (a former Porto car) passes the Empire, now re-erected in San Jose's Kelley Park.

San Jose Railroad 129 was brought back from rotting chicken-coop to fully operational condition in the 1980s. It is seen outside the San Jose light rail shops about to take up service on the downtown historic trolley loop in April 1990.

The Orange Empire Railway Museum's standard-gauge main line recreates the ambience of the old Pacific Electric Railway's interurban routes to the north and east of Los Angeles seventy or more years ago as this photo of PE combine 498 demonstrates. The car is trundling back to the museum from 11th street in Perris in April 1984.

Chicago

Chicago Transit Authority, PO Box 3555, Chicago IL 60654-3555. (312) 664-7200.

The CTA has operated Chicago's subway/elevated rapid transit and bus services since 1947. Its historic street cars were sold some years ago to the Illinois Railway Museum and the Fox River Trolley Musem. All historic buses (except for 8499) have been sold. A few survivors of the 1-50 and 6000-class PCC rapid transit cars remain on the property, either as work cars or as a reserve fleet for the Skokie Swift line. The CTA also maintains the following historic elevated and rapid transit cars.

RAPID TRANSIT CARS	BUILDER AND DATE	TRUCKS	CAR TYPE
South Side Rapid Transit 1	Jackson & Sharp, circa 1892	Unknown	DE DT Elevated trailer
(Originally a steam-hauled elevated trailer, motorized circa 1900, became a trailer again circa 1930.)			
South Side Rapid Transit 2007/08	Pullman-Standard, 1963	CTA-1	DE DT rapid transit
(These CTA cars carry a fake color scheme for their type.)			
Chicago RT 4271/72	Cincinnati, 1922	Baldwin 78-30	DE DT Elevated

South Elgin

Fox River Trolley Museum, PO Box 315, South Elgin, IL 60177-0315. (847) 697-4676. Standard-gauge trolley museum on route 31, six miles south of I-90, three miles south of U. S. 20. Cars run Sundays and holidays May-November 11:00 a.m.- 5:00 p.m., Saturdays in July and August 11:00 a.m.- 5:00 p.m.

This museum owns part of a never-closed segment of an early interurban, the Carpentersville, Elgin and Fox River Railway of 1896, later merged into the Aurora, Elgin and Fox River Electric Railway. Part of the line ran until 1972, hauling coal to the State Hospital at Elgin. In 1959, the Railway Equipment Leasing and Investment Company, a group preserving cars from the newly-closed Chicago, Aurora and Elgin interurban, contracted with the AE&FR to store cars on the railroad and operate them on weekends when freight services did not run. The first car ran July 4, 1966 and when the AE&FR lost its last customer and closed the line, RELIC bought the present segment, a scenic run on private right-of-way alongside the Fox River. RELIC became a not-for-profit operator in 1984 and changed its name to the Fox River Trolley Museum.

A. City and Suburban Cars

CARS	BUILDER AND DATE	TRUCKS	CAR TYPE
Chicago Ry. Co. 6	American, 1891	Brill 21-E	DE ST RPO mail car
(Originally Cicero & Proviso St. Ry. 6, rebuilt 1909 by West Chicago Ry. as mail car H-5.)			
Johnstown (PA) Traction Co. 362	St. Louis, 1926	St. Louis EDJ-64	DE DT Lightweight city
San Francisco MUNI 1030	St. Louis, 1951	St. Louis B-3	SE DT PCC

Rio de Janeiro (Brazil) 441, a single-truck 10-bench open and Rio 1719, a double-truck 13-bench open, both formerly at Fox River, are now stored at the Middlestown and Hummelstown Street Railway in Hummelstown PA.

B. Interurban Cars

Chicago, South Shore & South Bend 7/14	Pullman, 1926	Baldwin 84-60AA	DE DT Interurban coach
Chicago, Aurora & Elgin 20	Niles, 1902	Baldwin	DE DT Interurban coach
Chicago, Aurora & Elgin 316/17	Jewett, 1913	Baldwin 84-35AH	DE DT Interurban coach
Chicago, North Shore & Milwaukee 715/56	Cincinnati, 1926, Standard, 1930	Baldwin 84-30AA	DE DT Interurban coach

C. Rapid transit cars

Chicago CTA 4288, 4451	Cincinnati, 1922/24	Baldwin 78-30	DE DT Elevated
Chicago RT 5001 (later CTA 51)	Pullman-Standard, 1947	Clark B-2 Special	DE 3-section articulated PCC rapid transit
Chicago CTA 6101/02	St. Louis, 1950	Clark B-2	SE DT PCC rapid transit

34

Chicago CTA 4103 (Cincinnati, 1914s) is used to store parts and is not accessioned.

D. Work Cars and Locomotives

Chicago, Aurora & Elgin 11	Brill, 1910	Peckham	DE DT Line car
(Originally a box motor, became a line car in 1947.)			
Chicago CTA L-202	Chicago City Ry., 1908	Hedley	DE DT Steeple-cab locomotive

Philadelphia (SEPTA) snowsweeper C-150 was scrapped in 1991. Chicago CTA GM bus 605 went to the Illinois Railway Museum in 1996.

Union

Illinois Railway Museum, *7000 Olson Road, Union IL 60180. (815) 923-4391. Standard-gauge railroad, trolley and interurban museum, also runs ETBs and buses. Cars run daily Memorial Day-Labor Day, weekends May and September, Sundays April and October.*

The Indiana Railroad's last interurban line was abandoned in 1941. Electric railroad buffs, led by Chicago streetcar operator Howard Odinius, persuaded the Cedar Rapids and Iowa City (the CRANDIC) to buy an IR car for service as they couldn't keep a car as an historical artifact. Times had changed when the CRANDIC ceased passenger runs in 1953. Trolley museums were springing up like mushrooms after rain and what had been impossible in 1941 was no longer so. Odinius and his group bought back the car from the CRANDIC, started an Illinois Electric Railway Museum and began to buy more cars. The IERM became the IRM in 1962 once it began collecting railroad exhibits. The present site (its first permanent home) was bought in 1964, the first cars ran July 17, 1966. Over five miles of this former Elgin and Belvidere interurban line is in service, well-suited to the IRM's high-speed interurbans and heavy railroad trains. There is a separate one-mile streetcar loop on museum grounds, a Chicago "El" station and ETB operation on some of the internal roads.

The IRM's mission is to "demonstrate the vital role railroads have played in the growth of the Chicago area," by preserving and operating "railroad and mass transit rolling stock and their related artifacts" for the public in a realistic setting. A visitor has a bewildering choice of rides on many transit modes; an authentic experience of public transport in and around bygone Chicago. But the sheer size of the collection and Chicago's place as America's premier railroad city for more than one hundred and fifty years, make this one of the few rail transportation museums of national, rather than just regional, significance.

A. City and Suburban Cars

CARS	BUILDER AND DATE	TRUCKS	CAR TYPE
West Chicago Street Ry. 4	Pullman, 1895	Brill 21-E	DE ST City
North Chicago Street Ry. 8 (later 805)	Stephenson, 1859	Pedestal	SE ST Horse car
Gary (IN) Rys. 19	Cummings, 1927	Cummings 62	DE DT Lightweight "safety"
Illinois Terminal 101	American, 1917	St. Louis 61A	DE DT Center-entrance suburban
(Originally Alton, Granite & St. Louis 61, then St. Louis & Alton 61.)			
Chicago & West Towns 141	McGuire-Cummings, 1924	McGuire 10B	DE DT City
Chicago CSL 144	Pullman, 1908	Baldwin 150	DE DT City
(Originally Chicago City Railways 144.)			
Illinois Terminal 170	American, 1920	Brill 79-E-1	DE ST Birney "safety"
(Originally Galesburg [IL] Railway Lighting & Power 7, later used in Alton IL.)			
Indiana RR 205	Kuhlman, 1927	Brill 177-E-1X	DE DT "Safety"
Chicago City Ry. 209	CSL shops, 1934	Pedestal	DE ST Replica cable car trailer
Chicago & Milwaukee ER 354	St. Louis, 1928	St. Louis EIB 64	DE DT "Safety"
Illinois Terminal 415	St. Louis, 1924	St. Louis CM69	DE DT Lightweight suburban
(Originally Illinois Traction [Illinois Valley Division] 64, later Chicago and Illinois Valley 64.)			
Knoxville (TN) Power & Light 419	Cincinnati, 1925	–	DE ST Curveside lightweight "safety" (body only)
Chicago CSL 460	Pullman, 1908	Baldwin 150	DE DT City car
Milwaukee TMER&L 966/72	St. Louis, 1927	St. Louis EIB-64	DE DT "safety" City
Chicago CSL 1374	St. Louis, 1906	St. Louis 47	DE DT City
(Originally Chicago Union Traction Co. 4903.)			
Chicago CSL 1467	CUT,1899	Brill 27-G-E-1	DE DT City
(Originally Chicago Union Traction Co. 4512.)			
Philadelphia SEPTA 2267	St. Louis, 1946	Clark B-2	SE DT PCC
(Originally Kansas City PS 758.)			

Chicago CSL 2843	Jewett, 1903	Taylor	DE DT City
(Originally South Chicago City Railway 323.)			
Chicago CSL 2846	South Chicago City Ry. 1907 McGuire 10A		DE DT City
(Originally South Chicago City Railway 332.)			
Chicago CSL 3142	Brill, 1923	Brill 51-E-2	DE DT City
Chicago CSL 4001	Pullman-Standard, 1934	–	SE DT Experimental pre-PCC (body only)
Chicago CSL 4021	St. Louis, 1936	Clark B-2	SE DT PCC
Cleveland CTS 4223	Pullman-Standard, 1946	Clark B-2	SE DT MU PCC
(Later Toronto TTC type A-11 MU PCC 4648. Sold by TTC to Cleveland RTA in 1977 as Shaker 4648.)			
Chicago CTA 4391	St. Louis, 1948	St. Louis B-3	SE DT PCC
Chicago CSL 9020	Home-built, 1921	Brill 67-F	DE DT Trailer

Philadelphia Red Arrow 68 (Brill, 1926), San Francisco MUNI PCC 1183 (St. Louis, 1946, originally Kansas City PS 767, then Toronto TTC Type A-14 4763) and Toronto TTC PCC 4651 (Pullman-Standard, 1946, originally Cleveland CTS 4226), have been scrapped.

B. Interurban and Electric Freight Cars

Milwaukee TMER&L M-1	Home-built, 1917	TMER&L M100AB	DE DT Express Motor
Chicago, South Shore & South Bend 8	Pullman, 1926	Baldwin 84-60AA	DE DT Interurban coach
Milwaukee TMER&L M-15	Home-built, 1920	TMER&L M100AB	DE DT Express motor
Chicago, South Shore & South Bend 19	Pullman, 1926	Baldwin 84-60AA	DE DT Interurban coach
Michigan Electric 28	St. Louis, 1913	Baldwin 84-30AA	DE DT Combine
Chicago, South Shore & South Bend 28/34/37/40	Standard, 1929	Baldwin 84-30AA	DE DT Interurban coach
(Car 40 is on loan from the National Parks Service.)			
Indiana Railroad 65	Pullman-Standard, 1931	Commonwealth	SE DT Lightweight interurban coach
(Later Cedar Rapids and Iowa City Ry. 120.)			
Sand Springs (OK) Ry. 68	Cincinnati, 1918	Cincinnati arch bar	DE DT Lightweight interurban coach
(Originally Cincinnati, Lawrenceberg & Aurora [OH,IN] Electric Street RR 920.)			
Ft. Wayne, Van Wert & Lima (IN, OH) 91	St. Louis, 1924	–	DE DT Combine (body only)
Chicago, North Shore & Milwaukee 160	Brill, 1915	Brill 27-MCB-3X	DE DT Interurban coach
Chicago, North Shore & Milwaukee 213	Cincinnati, 1919	Baldwin 78-35AA	DE DT Box trailer
Chicago, North Shore & Milwaukee 218/29	Cincinnati, 1922	Baldwin 78-35AA	DE DT Box motor
Illinois Terminal 233	St. Louis, 1906	St. Louis 61A	SE DT Office car trailer
Illinois Terminal 234	Danville, 1910	St. Louis 102	SE DT Observation trailer
Chicago, North Shore & Milwaukee 251/53	Jewett, 1917	Baldwin 84-30AA	DE DT Combine
Interstate (IN, KY) PS of IN 266	Kuhlman, 1927	Brill 177	DE DT Lightweight interurban coach
(Later Indiana RR 204 in Terre Haute, then Portland Traction [OR] 4003.)			
Illinois Terminal 277	St. Louis, 1913	St. Louis 62	SE DT Combine
Aurora, Elgin & Fox River 306	St. Louis, 1924	St. Louis EIB-64	DE DT Lightweight interurban coach
Chicago, Aurora & Elgin 308/09	Niles, 1906/Hicks, 1908	Unknown	DE DT Interurban coach
Chicago Aurora & Elgin 321	Jewett, 1914	Baldwin 84-35AH	DE DT Interurban coach
Chicago Aurora & Elgin 431	Cincinnati, 1927	Baldwin 84-30AA	DE DT Interurban coach
Ft. Wayne & Wabash Valley Trctn. 504	Cincinnati, 1906	–	SE DT Interurban coach (body only)
(Later Ft. Wayne & Nthn. car, Indiana Traction Co. 354 "Talisman," later Indiana Service Corp. car.)			
Chicago South Shore & South Bend 504	St. Louis, 1925	Baldwin	DE DT Box trailer
(Originally Indiana Service Combine 377, later Indiana Service RPO 377).			
Illinois Terminal 504	ACF, 1910	ACF MCB	DE DT Sleeping car "Peoria"
Illinois Terminal 518	St. Louis, 1911	St. Louis 102 MCB	DE DT Interurban trailer car
Cincinnati & Lake Erie 640	Cincinnati, 1930	Taylor MCB	DE DT Express Motor
Chicago, North Shore & Milwaukee 714	Cincinnati, 1926	Baldwin 84-30AA	DE DT Interurban coach
Chicago, North Shore & Milwaukee 749	Pullman, 1928	Baldwin 84-35AA	DE DT Interurban coach

Chicago, North Shore & Milwaukee 757/63	Standard, 1930	Baldwin 84-30AA	DE DT Interurban coach
Chicago, North Shore & Milwaukee 801/2	St. Louis, 1941	GSI Commonwealth cast steel	DE 4-section articulated "Electroliner"

(Became Philadelphia Suburban/SEPTA [P&W] "Valley Forge" in 1964.)

Lake Shore Electric (OH) 810	Kuhlman, 1924	–	DT Box trailer

(Formerly Michigan Electric Ry. interurban freight trailer 1616.)

Milwaukee TMER&L 1129	Home-built, 1924	Baldwin 84-34AA	SE DT Interurban coach
Milwaukee TMER&L 1135	Home-built, 1924	Standard C-80P2	SE DT Parlor car "Menominee"

Chicago, North Shore & Milwaukee box motor 237 and combine 250 (the latter acquired from the Wisconsin Electric Railway Historical Society in 1988) have been scrapped for parts.

C. Rapid Transit Cars

Chicago CTA 52	Pullman-Standard, 1947	Clark B-2 special	DE 3-section articulated PCC rapid transit

(Originally Chicago Rapid Transit 5002.)

Philadelphia SEPTA 55	Brill, 1927	Commonwealth	DE DT "Broad Street" subway
Chicago RT 1024	Pullman, 1898	McGuire "Hedley"	DE DT Elevated
Illinois Central RR 1198	Pullman, 1926	Commonwealth MCB	DE DT Commuter
Chicago RT 1268	ACF, 1907	McGuire "Hedley"	DE DT Elevated trailer
Illinois Central 1380	Pullman, 1926	Commonwealth MCB	DE DT Commuter trailer
Chicago RT 1754	Jewett, 1906	Baldwin 78-30	DE DT Elevated
Chicago RT 1797, 1808	ACF, 1907	McGuire "Hedley"	DE DT Elevated
Chicago CTA 2153/54	Pullman-Standard, 1964	CTA-1	SE DT Rapid transit
Chicago RT 2872/88	Pullman, 1906	Baldwin MCB	DE DT Elevated
Chicago CTA 4146	Cincinnati, 1915	Baldwin 78-30	DE DT Elevated
Chicago CTA 4290, 4321	Cincinnati, 1922	Baldwin 78-30	DE DT Elevated
Chicago RT 4410/12	Cincinnati, 1924	Baldwin 78-30	DE DT Elevated
Chicago CTA 6125/26	St. Louis, 1950	Clark B-2	SE DT PCC Rapid transit
Chicago CTA 6461/62	St. Louis, 1955	St. Louis B-3	SE DT PCC Rapid transit
Chicago CTA 6655/56	St. Louis, 1957	St. Louis B-3	SE DT PCC Rapid transit

Philadelphia SEPTA subway car 126 was not accessioned and was scrapped for parts.

D. Work Cars and Locomotives

Milwaukee TMER&L L-3	Home-built, 1920	TMER&L M100AB	DE DT Steeple-cab locomotive
Chicago CSL X-4	Home-built, 1946	Arch bar	SE DT Crane/Flat car with cab

(Originally Chicago Ry. N-2 Dump car [McGuire-Cummings 1910].)

Commonwealth Edison 4	Alco/GE, 1911	Alco articulated	DE DT Steeple-cab locomotive
Milwaukee TMER&L L-4	Home-built, 1920	TMER&L M100AB	DE ST Steeple-cab locomotive
Milwaukee TMER&L L-7	Home-built, 1931	Brill MCB	DE DT Steeple-cab locomotive
Milwaukee TMER&T L-10	Home-built, 1944	TMER&L M100AB	DE DT Steeple-cab locomotive
Milwaukee TMER&L 12	Home-built, 1926	TMER&L M35AB	DT Portable substation
Milwaukee TMER&L D-13	Differential, 1920	TMER&L M100AB	DE DT Differential side-dump
Cornwall (ON) Ry. & Light 14	Baldwin/WH, 1929	Baldwin	DE DT Type B-1 locomotive

(Originally Springfield [VT] Terminal Railway 20.)

Milwaukee TMER&L D-16	Brown, 1923	TMER&L M100AB	DE DT Locomotive crane
Milwaukee TMER&L D-22	Home-built, 1907	St. Louis 23AE	DE DT Line car
Milwaukee TMER&L M-26	St. Louis, 1903	Brill MCB	DT Unmotored flat
Iowa Terminal 30	McGuire-Cummings, 1915	McGuire 10A	DE DT Steeple-cab locomotive

(Later Charles City & Western 300).

Milwaukee TMER&L M-37	Home-built, 1931	St. Louis 23A	DT Unmotored container car
Milwaukee TMER&L B-48	Home-built, 1926	St. Louis 23MC	DE DT Snow sweeper
Milwaukee TMER&L E-58	Home-built, 1907	TMER&L 5'11" Arch bar	DT Unmotored flat
Milwaukee TMER&L E-117	Unknown	Bettendorf T-iron	DT Unmotored flat

(This car was bought used in 1931.)

Milwaukee TMER&L F-208	Differential, 1921	TMER&L 5'11" Arch bar	DT Side dump trailer

(Later motored and numbered D-15.)

Chicago CSL E-223	McGuire-Cummings, 1908	McGuire Pedestal	DE ST Snow sweeper

(Originally Chicago City Ry. E-23.)

Chicago CSL F-305	Home-built, 1930	McGuire 10A	DE DT Snow Plow

(Originally Calumet & South Chicago Ry. D-303 [Mcguire-Cummings 1910] sprinkler car.)

Chicago CTA S-309	Home-built, unknown date	Baldwin MCB	DT Unmotored flat with cabs

(Originally CSL W-223, rebuilt to present configuration by CTA in 1953.)

Chicago CTA S-373	Cincinnati, 1924	Baldwin 78-30	DE EL Work motor and line car

(Originally CTA 4411)

D. Work Cars and Locomotives, *continued*

Chicago, North Shore & Milwaukee 604	Chicago & Milwaukee, 1914	McGuire 20A	DE DT Line car
Chicago, South Shore & South Bend 803	GE, 1949	GSI cast steel	DE "Little Joe" articulated locomotive
Chicago, North Shore & Milwaukee 1502 *(Later Chicago CTA S-107.)*	Standard, 1926	Arch bar	DT Unmotored piggyback flat
Illinois Traction 1565	Home-built, 1910	Alco RM-63B	DE DT Class B locomotive
Illinois Terminal 1702 *(Originally IT "Pull car" 1507, rebuilt as line car 1702 in 1922.)*	Danville Ry. & Light, 1903	St. Louis 61A	DE DT Line car
Amtrak (Pennsylvania RR) 4939 *(Originally Pennsylvania RR 4927).*	PRR/GE, 1942	GSI cast steel	Type GG-1 articulated main line locomotive

E. Electric Trolley Buses

BUS	BUILDER AND DATE	SERIAL NUMBER
Chicago CSL 84	Brill (American) T40, 1930	—
Chicago CTA 192/93 (later 9192/93)	Brill 40SMT, 1937	364/65
Des Moines (IA) TC 239	Brill TC44, 1948	527
Milwaukee M&ST 269	St. Louis, 1941	–
Dayton CTC 435	Pullman 44CX, 1947	–
Milwaukee and Suburban Tnspt. 441	Marmon-Herrington TC44, 1948	10517
Cleveland CTS 874	Pullman 44CX, 1948	–
(Originally Providence [RI] United Electric Railway 1428, then United Transit 8537.)		
Chicago CTA 9553, 9631 (originally 553, 631)	Marmon-Herrington TC49, 1951	15105, 15203
Chicago CTA 9763 (originally 999)	Twin Coach 58 DWTT, 1948	001 (articulated ETB)

F. Motor Buses

Chicago, North Shore & Milwaukee 10/11	White 31S, unknown date	– (Gasoline)
Montebello (CA) Municipal Lines 17 *(Originally assigned by Office of Defense Transportation to Lang Motor Bus, Long Beach CA. later Ontario [CA] MUNI Lines.)*	Ford Transit/Union City, 1944	– (Gasoline)
Chicago CTA 605 *(This bus was formerly at the Fox River Museum in South Elgin, IL)*	GM, 1951	– (Diesel)
Chicago CSL 3407	White 798, 1944	290805 (Gasoline)

INDIANA

Fort Wayne

Three Rivers Heritage Council, *PO Box 12828, Fort Wayne, IN 46866-2828. (219) 426-7245.*

The THRC's goal is to purchase, stabilize and restore the former New York Central RR freight house at Clinton and Fourth in Fort Wayne, across from Lawton Park, midway between the new flood plain park, Headwaters Park and Science Central. Immediately adjacent to the freight house is track owned and operated by the city of Fort Wayne which will become the Headwaters-Heartland Electric Railway, providing trolley service among the parking lots of five area tourist destinations. The TRHC owns the body of Fort Wayne city car 511 (St. Louis, 1923) which will be cosmetically restored and displayed at the Heartland RR Museum (the museum being established by the TRHC). Two other cars of the same 500-545 series have been found recently and are being bought.

Michigan City

RAIL Foundation, *1101 Franklin Street, Michigan City, IN 46360. Proposed interpretive center and tourist trolley.*

In November 1996, RAIL and Michigan City were awarded almost $700,000 as part of an ISTEA enhancement grant to remodel the former Haskell and Barker Car and Manufacturing Company's brass foundry into an interurban railway interpretive center. Target opening date is late-1997. Cars to be displayed include Chicago, South Shore and South Bend RR 6, 33 and 107 (see Noblesville IN entry), belonging to the National Park Service, Indiana Dunes National Lakeshore unit. The NPS bought these and sixteen other South Shore cars in 1983 for a proposed tourist line serving the Indiana Dunes. This line is scheduled as the second stage of the Interurban Railway Interpretive Center project. Under the name "Trolley to the Dunes," it will run from the interpretive center in Michigan City to the Indiana Dunes National Lakeshore at Mt. Baldy. No start or completion date for this line has yet been announced.

Noblesville

Indiana Transportation Museum, PO Box 83, Noblesville, IN 46060-0083. (317) 773-6000. Standard-gauge rail and trolley museum in Noblesville, twenty miles north of Indianapolis on route 19. Cars run weekends and holidays April-November noon-5:00pm.

A regional rail transportation museum based in Noblesville's Forest Park, the ITM collects local (Indianapolis region) street railway and interurban equipment for display and operation in the park. Much of the railroad passenger equipment and locomotives are regularly operated in main-line passenger excursion service from the park.

A. City and Suburban Cars

CARS	BUILDER AND DATE	TRUCKS	CAR TYPE
Indianapolis Street Railway 1	Unkown, 1868	Pedestal	DE ST Mule car
Indianapolis Railways 153	Brill, 1932	–	DE DT Lightweight city (body only)

Toronto TTC 4480 (St. Louis/CCF, 1949, SE DT Type A-7 MU PCC) and Toronto TTC 4556 (St. Louis, 1947 DE ST Type A-9 PCC, (originally Cincinnati Street Railway Co. 1156) are being scrapped for parts.

B. Interurban Cars

Terre Haute, Indianapolis & Estn. 81	Jewett, 1902	–	DE DT Interurban coach (body only)
(In 1995 this car was believed to be at the Hoosier Valley RR Museum in North Judson, IN.)			
Chicago, North Shore & Milwaukee 172	Cincinnati, 1919	Baldwin 84-30AA	DE DT Interurban coach
Union Traction (IN) 429/37	St. Louis, 1925	–	SE DT Combines "Noblesville" and "Marion" (bodies only)
Indianapolis & Cincinnati Traction 606	Cincinnati, 1923	–	SE DT Combine (body only)

The following South Shore cars have passed through the museum over the years.

Chicago, South Shore & South Bend 2/3/4/6	Pullman, 1926	Baldwin 84-60AA	DE DT Interurban coach
Chicago, South Shore & South Bend 33	Standard, 1929	Baldwin 84-60AA	DE DT Trailer
Chicago, South Shore & South Bend 107/08	Pullman, 1926	Baldwin 84-60AA	DE DT Combine

Car 6, 33 and 107 are owned by the U. S. National Parks Service (see Michigan City IN entry.) They were restored for the Parks Service by the ITM. Car 108 is now at the Hoosier Valley RR Museum, North Judson IN. CA&E 308 was sold to the Illinois Railway Museum in 1996.

C. Rapid Transit Cars

Chicago CTA 4293, 4454	Cincinnati, 1922/1926	Baldwin 78-30	DE DT Elevated

D. Work Cars and Locomotives

Singer Sewing Machine 1	GE, 1898	GE	DE ST locomotive
Mishawaka (IN) Twin Branch RR 4	Baldwin/WH, 1928	Unknown	DE DT Steeple-cab locomotive
Cedar Rapids & Iowa City 55	Detroit United, 1926	Standard C60-P	DE DT Locomotive
(Originally a Detroit United Railway locomotive.)			
Chicago CTA C-606	Cincinnati, 1922	Baldwin 84-30AA	DE EL Line car

Boone

East Side Electric Traction (*Iowa RR Historical Society, Boone & Scenic Valley RR*) *PO Box 603, Boone, IA 50036. (512) 432-4249. Standard-gauge tourist trolley runs from 10th and Division Street railroad station. Runs weekends and holidays Memorial Day-end of October 11:00 a.m.- 5:00 p.m.*

The Boone & Scenic Valley RR was established in 1983 by local business people and residents dedicated to preserving Boone's railroad heritage. Boone was a major division point on the Chicago and Northwestern RR and on the Fort Dodge, Des Moines & Southern, an interurban whose last electric cars ran on August 31, 1955. Acquired by the C&NW, the Fort Dodge line was leased in 1971 and closed in 1983. In 1984, the B&SV bought 11 miles of former Fort Dodge trackage. Today the B&SV's steam and diesel-hauled passenger trains run on these tracks, which feature the 156' tall "High Bridge" over the Des Moines River valley, the tallest on any North American interurban. East Side Electric Traction is the B&SV's electric division. It runs from the railroad station at 10th and Division Street along "back alley" city tracks to the former Fort Dodge interurban station, passing close to the birthplace of former First Lady Mamie Eisenhower.

CAR	BUILDER AND DATE	TRUCKS	CAR TYPE
Chicago, South Shore & South Bend 38/39	Standard, 1929	Baldwin 84-60AA	DE DT Trailer
Charles City Western Ry. 50	McGuire-Cummings, 1915	McGuire-Cummings C20A	DE DT Combine
(Later became Iowa Terminal RR 101.)			
Chicago, South Shore & South Bend 102/06/09	Pullman, 1926	Baldwin 84-60AA	DE DT Combine
Des Moines 512	McGuire-Cummings, 1915	–	SE DT City car (body only)

Clear Lake

Iowa Trolley Park (*Mason City & Clear Lake Railway Historical Society*), *PO Box 956, Mason City, IA 50401.(515) 357-7433. Park on Main Avenue, Clear Lake, west of 40th Street. Standard-gauge tourist trolley runs weekends Memorial Day-Labor Day.*

The Society is a tenant of the Iowa Traction RR, one of the last surviving electric interurban freight operators in the country and current owner of the former Mason City & Clear Lake line. The MC&CLRHS was set up in 1987 and ran passenger cars between Mason City, Emery and Clear Lake (over the 11 miles of Iowa Traction trackage) between 1988 and 1994. A car house and loop have been built on museum property just east of Clear Lake.

CAR	BUILDER AND DATE	TRUCKS	CAR TYPE
Iowa Terminal RR 3	McGuire-Cummings, 1911	McGuire-Cummings	DE ST Snow Sweeper
(Originally Mason City & Clear Lake 102, at Midwest Electric, Mount Pleasant IA from 1973 to 1989.)			
Chicago, North Shore & Milwaukee 727	Cincinnati, 1926	Baldwin 84-30AA	DE DT Interurban coach
(Later Iowa Terminal RR 102.)			
San Francisco MUNI 1146	St. Louis, 1946	Clark B-2	SE DT PCC
(Originally St. Louis PS 1763.)			
New Haven RR 28	unknown, circa 1896	–	DE DT commuter car (body only)

Gomaco 1976, a replica 15-bench Brill open (Gomaco 1982, Melbourne Type 1 trucks) was returned to Gomaco in the Fall of 1995.

Emery

Iowa Traction Railroad, *PO Box 309, Mason City, IA 50402-0309. (515) 424-4600. Standard-gauge trolley freight line with irregularly scheduled operation.*

The ITRR is the currrent owner of the former Mason City & Clear Lake Railroad, which opened between the two towns in 1897. Passenger cars were replaced by buses in January 1937 and street trackage in Clear Lake was abandoned in 1963, but freight trains continue to roll on this, Iowa's only surviving electric interurban freight railroad.

Work Cars and Locomotives

CAR	BUILDER AND DATE	TRUCKS	CAR TYPE
33	Cincinnati, 1922	Baldwin 78-35AA	DE DT Tool & Line car
(Originally Chicago, North Shore & Milwaukee Box motor 234.)			
50	Baldwin/WH Class B	Baldwin MCB	DE DT Locomotive
(Originally Monongahela West Penn locomotive, then Kansas City & Kaw Valley RR 505.)			
51	Baldwin/WH Class B	Baldwin MCB	DE DT Locomotive
(Originally Monongahela West Penn locomotive, then Kansas City & Kaw Valley RR 506.)			
53	Texas Electric, 1928	Unknown	DE DT locomotive
(Originally a Texas Electric locomotive.)			
54	Baldwin/WH Class B	Baldwin MCB	DE DT Locomotive
(Originally Iowa Southern 400.)			
60	Unknown	Unknown	DE DT Locomotive
(Originally Mason City & Clear Lake RR 60.)			

Mount Pleasant

Midwest Electric Railway Association, *1887 Thresher's Road, Mount Pleasant, IA 52641. (319) 385-8937. Standard-gauge tourist trolley. Cars run Sundays Memorial Day-August, daily Thursday-Monday on Labor day weekend.*

The MERA is a confederation of the Iowa Railway Historical Museum and the Midwest Old Settlers & Threshers' Association. In the 1960s, the IRHM ran a small collection of historic cars over the Southern Iowa Railway between Centerville and Moravia. The line was closed and sold in 1966 and the cars dispersed, one being destroyed by fire soon after. The Old Threshers and the IRHM agreed in 1968 to create an internal transit system on the Old Threshers' campgrounds at Mount Pleasant. These are packed to capacity at the Old Threshers' annual Labor Day weekend reunion: a gigantic salute to rural America, farm life and steam agricultural machinery (all operable). The first segment opened in 1971 and the present 1.1 mile loop around the campgrounds in 1974. Over the Labor Day weekend, 50,000 people ride between the campground and the Reunion's main gates up to a 1/2 mile away.

A. City and Suburban Cars

CAR	BUILDER AND DATE	TRUCKS	CAR TYPE
Waterloo, Cedar Falls & Nthn. (IA) 381	Perley Thomas, 1930	Brill 77-E-1	DE DT Lightweight city
(Originally Knoxville [TN] 379.)			
Old Threshers 1718, 1779	Rio de Janeiro, 1912	Unknown	DE DT 13-bench open
(Originally Rio de Janeiro [Brazil] Power & Light 1718, 1779 then Magee Transportation Museum of Bloomsburg PA. 1 and 2.)			
Boston MBTA 3093, 3226	Pullman-Standard, 1944/45	Clark B-2	SE DT MU PCC
Toronto TTC 4476	St. Louis/CCF, 1949	Clark B-2	SE DT MU Type A-7 PCC

B. Interurban Cars

Southern Iowa Ry. 9	Barber, 1909	Unknown	DE DT Interurban coach
(Originally had a Barber single truck until replaced by double trucks in 1915.)			
Chicago, Aurora & Elgin 320	Jewett, 1914	Baldwin 84-35HH	DE DT Interurban coach

C. Work Cars and Locomotives

Boston MBTA 3279	Home-built, 1910	Unknown	DE DT wire and utility car
(Originally ran on streetcar lines, transferred to Blue Line rapid transit in 1950, acquired by MERA in 1995.)			

Chicago EL cars 4258, 4420 (Cincinnati, 1922 and 1924) were bought for spares in the 1970s and scrapped in 1991.

KANSAS

Wichita

Great Plains Transportation Museum, *PO Box 2017-C, Wichita, KS 67201. (316) 263-0944. Regional transportation museum.*

This not-for-profit organization was established to preserve and display transportation equipment of significance in the development of the Wichita area. Collection began in the early 1970s and exhibits are mostly railroad artifacts displayed in Wichita Union Station at 701 E. Douglas Avenue. A restored Arkansas Valley Interurban Railway Co. depot of 1911 is also on display.

CAR	BUILDER AND DATE	TRUCKS	CAR TYPE
Arkansas Valley (KS) Interurban Ry. 12	Unknown	–	DE DT Express Motor (body only)
Wichita Transportation Co. 271		Twin Coach, 1954	– Diesel bus
(Sold to Springfield Mo. in 1960, returned to Wichita in 1980.)			
Wichita Gas & Electric unnumbered	Unknown, circa 1913	Unknown	DE DT Motor flat, used as locomotive

KENTUCKY

Covington Behringer-Crawford Museum of Natural History, *PO Box 67, Covington KY 41012.*

Brill-built 1892 city car 64 of the Cincinnati, Newport & Covington Railway, later rebuilt as parlor car "Kentucky" and displayed in Devou Park for many years, is being restored by the Transit Authority of Northern Kentucky for display at the BCMNH.

LOUISIANA

New Orleans

New Orleans RTA, *6700 Plaza Drive, New Orleans, LA 70127. (504) 242-2600.*

1. Riverfront Line Tourist Trolley, *5' 2 1/2" gauge. Runs daily all year.*

Since opening on August 14, 1988, this two-mile tourist line along the Mississippi riverfront has exceeded all ridership projections. It serves almost every downtown attraction including Canal Street, the French Quarter, the river, casinos and major hotels and is laid out on the tracks of the Public Belt Railway, which still runs alongside. The RTA in 1995 decided to integrate it with the St. Charles line (see below) by re-gauging to 5' 2 1/2" and building a connection on Canal Street to link the two, so reviving part of the old Canal line which closed in 1964. Riverfront closed for regauging in 1997. The Melbourne cars have been sold to Memphis.

CAR	BUILDER AND DATE	TRUCKS	CAR TYPE
Riverfront 450/51 (originally NOPSI 919, 924)	Perley Thomas, 1924	Brill 76-E-2	DE DT Lightweight city
Riverfront 452/54/55	M&MTB, 1930/1928/ Holden, 1926	Melbourne Type 1 (454 Type 1B)	DE DT Type W2 (454 SW2) drop-center city
(Originally Melbourne (Australia) M&MTB 626, 478, 371.)			
Riverfront 456/57 (originally NOPSI 952, 957)	Perley Thomas, 1924	Brill 76-E-2	DE DT Lightweight city
(457 has been remodeled with a wheelchair entrance and PCC trucks.)			

2. St. Charles Line *Heritage light rail, 5' 2 1/2" gauge. Runs daily year-round.*

This surviving first-generation street railway links the Garden District, Tulane University and downtown (including the western edge of the French Quarter) using state-of-the-art 1920s equipment and technology. It is to New Orleans what the cable cars are to San Francisco; a city symbol known world-wide. The line was rehabilitated in the late 1980s, with all-new track and foundations. In the early 1990s the cars were rebuilt as closely as possible to original condition cosmetically, but maintaining modern standards in mechanical and electrical equipment. Controllers, for example, are new-built replicas of a 1920s design. Recent funding problems have meant a slight reduction of service on the St. Charles line: several cars are temporarily stored out of service.

CAR	BUILDER AND DATE	TRUCKS	CAR TYPE
29	St. Louis, 1898	Brill 21-E	DE ST Work car (former passenger car)

| 453 | American, 1906 | Unknown | DE DT Semi-convertible |

(Originally numbered 303, became 453 in 1917. Now on static display at the Mint Building as a Desire car.)

900/03-7/10/11/14/15/20-23/26/30/32-34/37/40/45/47/48/51/53/54/61-63/65/68/69/71/72

| | Perley Thomas, 1924 | Brill 76-E-2 | DE DT Lightweight city |

Philadelphia SEPTA PCC 2147/66/83 (St. Louis, 1948) and 2737/49/51/79/88/91 (St. Louis, 1947) were bought for parts to be used in rebuilt and new replica Perley Thomas bodies. Car 957 (Riverfront 457) has been fitted with PCC equipment. At press time seven new replica Perley Thomas bodies were under construction and the RTA had accepted a bid from the Tatra Company in Prague for seven pairs of trucks and controls. PCC 2147 made a test run from the carhouse to Lee Circle in early 1995. Rio de Janeiro (Brazil) open car 1794 (home-built 1913) was sold to Memphis in 1996. It was once at the Connecticut Trolley Museum (Warehouse Point) East Windsor, was sold to Chattanooga Choo Choo in the mid-1970s and sold to New Orleans in 1989.

MAINE

Kennebunkport

Seashore Trolley Museum (New England Electric Railway Historical Society), *Drawer A, Kennebunkport, ME 04046-1690. (207) 967-2712 or 967-2800. Standard-gauge trolley museum at 195 Log Cabin Road, Kennebunkport ME 04046. Cars run daily May-mid-October, weekends mid-November, plus Santa specials.*

The world's first trolley museum, the NEERHS began in 1939 after a farewell trip on the Biddeford and Saco. An ad-hoc group of riders bought a B&S open car to preserve it in working order. That meant finding somewhere with room for a trolley track. The roadbed of the Atlantic Shore Line between Biddeford and Kennebunkport still existed and the group moved onto the present site in 1940. Initially they were to preserve something of the New England trolley. But the decimation of North America's trolleys between 1945 and 1970 prompted a radical change. Soon after the first car ran on December 27, 1953, the NEERHS set out to become the "National Collection of American Streetcars," hoping to collect at least one car from each state and major city, plus examples of all other mass transit modes: interurbans, buses, subways, rapid transit and ETBs. Thus Seashore is now America's national museum of mass transit.

Yet its regional New England collection is unsurpassed, with the finest collection of Boston transit artifacts anywhere. An international collection supplements the North American exhibits and the on-going "Operation Last Round-up" locates, identifies and brings to the museum surviving North American cars hitherto believed extinct. Its tracks will ultimately reach Biddeford, five miles away. In 1982, a separate Biddeford Station Corporation was chartered to develop and operate Seashore's future north terminal at no chargeable expense to the NEERHS. Building and development was well advanced in 1996 and a 2' gauge tourist railroad has been installed. The present terminal at Talbott Park (dedicated October 7, 1995) two miles short of Biddeford Station, is being developed as a trolley park to illustrate the custom of building parks at the edge of town, accessible only by trolley, to encourage evening and weekend riding. (*= 3'6" gauge)

A. City and Suburban Cars

CAR	BUILDER AND DATE	TRUCKS	CAR TYPE
Manchester (NH) "City of Manchester"	Briggs, 1898	Brill 21-E	DE ST Parlor
Denver & South Platte 1	American, 1919	Brill 78-M	DE ST Birney "safety"
(Later York [ME] Utilities 80). On loan to Valentine Museum, Riverside Campus, Richmond VA as VA Transit Co. {Richmond} 1283.)			
Montreal Tramways 2	Home-built, 1906	Brill 27-G	SE DT Open sightseeing
Brattleboro (VT) 8	Wason, 1917	Brill 21-E	DE ST City
Fitchburg (MA) 8	Brill, 1886	Pedestal	DE ST 7-bench open horse car
(Later Templeton [MA] Street Railway car, then Northern Massachusetts Street Railway 12.)			
Newport & Providence (RI) 9	Laconia, 1904	–	DE DT 15-bench open (body only)
New Bedford, Union St. Ry. 10	Brill, 1885	Brill pedestal	DE ST Horse car
Biddeford and Saco 31	Brill, 1900	Brill 22-E	DE DT 12-bench open

43

Manchester and Nashua (NH) 38	Laconia, 1906	Laconia 8B	DE DT Suburban
Wheeling (WV) 39	Cincinnati, 1924	Standard C-35P	DE DT "Curved-side" city
Middlesex & Boston 41	Stephenson, 1901	–	DE ST City (body only)
Sioux City (IA) Service Co. 46	Home-built, 1914	–	DE DT City (body only)
*San Francisco, Cal. Cable 48	Holman, 1907	Home-built arch bar	DE DT "California" cable car
Mobile (AL) Light & RR 49	Perley Thomas, 1930	–	DE ST Lightweight city (body only)
Mass. Northeastern 50	Laconia, 1902	Laconia 8B	DE DT Suburban
Roanoke (VA) 51	Brill, 1929		DE DT "Master Unit" city (body only)

(Originally Lynchburg [VA] 115.)

Manchester (NH) 60 (originally 70)	Laconia, 1895	–	DE ST City (body only)
Waterville Fairfield & Oakland (ME) 60	Brill, 1922	–	DE DT Birney "safety" (body only)

(Originally Plymouth & Brockton [MA] Street Railway 400.)

Philadelphia Suburban (Red Arrow) 62	Brill, 1927	Brill 27-MCB-3X	DE DT Center-entrance MU suburban
York (ME) Utilities 82	American, 1919	Brill 78-M	DE ST Birney "safety"

(Originally Denver and South Platte [CO] 2.

*Denver Tramways 83	Woeber, 1906	–	DE DT Center-entrance city
York (ME) Utilities 88	Wason, 1926	Brill 177-E1X	DE DT Lightweight city
Dunedin (New Zealand) 105 (originally 5)	Stansfield, 1905	Unknown	DE ST Cable grip
Nagasaki, Japan 134	Japan Rolling Stock, 1911	Brill 21-E	DE ST City
Blackpool (England) Corporation 144	Home-built, 1925	Blackpool/Hurst Nelson "Preston"	DE DT Open-balcony double-deck city
Richmond, VA. Electric Power 194	Southern, 1910	–	DE DT City (body only)

(Originally Richmond and Henrico Railway car.)

Philadelphia SEPTA (P&W) 203/08	Brill, 1931	Brill 89-E-2	DE DT "Bullet" lightweight suburban
Chicago CTA 225	Pullman, 1908	Baldwin 150	DE DT City
Boston, West End St. Ry. 235	Laconia, 1895	Brill 21-E	DE ST City
Rome (Italy) 279	Tabanelli, 1914	Unknown radial	DE ST City
Liverpool (England) Corporation 293	Home-built, 1939	EMB hornless	DE ST Double deck city
Atlantic City 299`	St. Louis, 1925	–	DE DT Lightweight city (body only)

(Originally Fort Wayne [IN] 552.)

Connecticut Co. 303 (later 615)	Brill, 1901	Standard 0-50	DE DT 15-bench open
Pusan (South Korea) 352	Cincinnati, 1927	Brill 177-E-2X	DE DT Lightweight city

(Originally Atlanta Power and Light unidentified 860-class car. Car sold to Korea Electric 1949, became Pusan 352 until 1968 then a diner in Las Vegas NV, to museum in 1988. Original trucks, narrowed to 3'6" gauge in Pusan, now at Orange Empire Railway Museum.

Boston, West End St. Ry. 396	St. Louis, 1900	Peckham 14B4	DE DT City car
Knoxville (TN) Ry. & Lt. 410	Cincinnati, 1925	–	DE ST "Curved-side" city (body only)
Dallas Railway & Terminal 434	American, 1914	Brill 39-E-1	DE DT Stone & Webster city
Boston ER 475	Newburyport, 1903	Taylor LB	DE DT City
Rochester Division, NY State Rys. 502	Brill, 1904	–	DE DT Semi-convertible (body only)
*LARY 521	St. Louis, 1906	LARY T-3	DE DT Type BF California
Leeds (England) Corporation 526	UCC, 1931	EMB/English Electric Type 4	DE DT Double deck city

(Originally Metropolitan Tramways Co. [London] 341, London Transport 2085 in 1933, Leeds 526 in 1950.)

Dallas 608 (later Boston 3342)	Pullman-Standard, 1945	Clark B-2	DE DT PCC
Biddeford & Saco 615	Wason, 1920	–	DE ST Birney "safety" (body only)
New York TARS 631	Home-built, 1939	Brill 77-E	DE DT Lightweight city

(Later Wiener Stadtwerke Verkehrsbetriebe [Vienna, Austria] Type Z 4216.)

Wheeling (WV) 639	Cincinnati, 1924	Standard C-35P	DE DT "Curved-side" city

PE 680	St. Louis, 1924	–	DE DT "Hollywood" suburban (body only)
(Renumbered PE 5069 in 1949, became Portland Traction [OR] 4022 in 1953.)			
Boston, West End St. Ry. 724	Metropolitan, 1884	Brill 21-E	DE ST City
(Rebuilt as an electric car from a horsecar in 1893, by splicing and lengthening.)			
Oakland (CA) Key System 804	Home-built, 1919	–	DE DT Lightweight city (body only)
Harrisburg Rys. (PA) 811	Brill, 1917	–	DE DT Semi-convertible (body only)
Ottawa TC 825	Ottawa, 1925	–	DE DT Lightweight city (body only)
Connecticut Co. 838	Jones, 1905	Taylor SP	DE DT 15-bench open
Milwaukee TMERL 861	St. Louis, 1921	TMERL M35AB	DE DT Lightweight city
Kansas City PS 922	Cincinnati, 1911	–	DE DT city (body only)
Boston, West End St. Ry. 925	Jones, 1894	Brill 21-E	DE ST Parlor
Montreal Tramways 957	Ottawa, 1911	Brill 27 FE1	SE DT City
New Orleans PSI 966	Perley Thomas, 1924	–	DE DT Lightweight city
(Acquired from Heart of Dixie NRHS Chapter, Birmingham [AL] circa 1982.)			
Boston, West End St. Ry. 1059	Barney & Smith, 1895	West End 57E	DE ST City
San Francisco MUNI 1155	St. Louis, 1946	Clark B-2	SE DT PCC
(Originally St. Louis PS 1726 and scheduled to be restored as such.)			
Connecticut Co. 1160 (originally 542)	Stephenson, 1906	Standard C-50	DE DT City
Rochester (NY) 1213	Cincinnati, 1916	–	SE DT "Peter Witt" city (body only)
Cleveland Ry. 1227 (later Shaker Hts. 27)	Kuhlman, 1915	–	SE DT Center-entrance city (body only)
Twin Cities (MN) TCRT 1267	Transit Supply, 1907	Twin Cities 9RB (Baldwin 5)	SE DT Type H-6 "Gate" city
Glasgow (Scotland) Corporation 1274	Home-built, 1941	EMB Lightweight L5	DE DT Double-deck city
D.C. Transit 1304	St. Louis, 1941	Clark B-2	SE DT PCC
Connecticut Co. 1391 (originally 317)	Osgood-Bradley, 1910	Standard 0-50	DE DT 15-bench open
Pittsburgh Railway 1440	St. Louis, 1942	Clark B-2	SE DT PCC
Connecticut Co. 1468 (originally 167)	Osgood-Bradley, 1911	Standard 0-50	DE DT 15-bench open
Sydney (Australia) 1700	Meadowbank, 1926	Sydney 9	DE DT Type P city
Montreal Tramways 2052	Wason, 1927	Brill 177-E-2X	DE DT Lightweight city
(Originally Springfield [MA] 570.)			
Cincinnati St. Ry. 2105	Cincinnati, 1917	–	DE DT City (body only)
Cleveland Railway 2318	Home-built, 1918	Brill 67-F	SE DT Center-entrance trailer
Montreal Tramways 2652	CCF, 1930	CCF	SE DT Lightweight city
Philadelphia SEPTA 2709	St. Louis, 1947	Clark B-2	SE DT PCC
Hamburg (Germany) 2710	Unknown, 1921	Unknown	SE ST City
Boston MBTA 3019/83/127/221	Pullman-Standard, 1941/45/44/46	Clark B-2	SE DT MU PCC
Lynn & Boston St. Railway 3256	Brill, 1888	–	DE ST 8-bench open (body only)
(Originally a horse car.)			
Boston MBTA 3274/92	Pullman-Standard, 1951	Clark B-2	SE DT MU PCC
Boston MBTA 3340	Pullman-Standard, 1945	Clark B-2	DE DT PCC
(Formerly Dallas Railway & Terminal 615.)			
Boston MBTA 3400	Home-built, 1971	–	Mock-up of proposed Type 6 light rail vehicle
Berlin (Germany) 3412	Unknown, 1927	Unknown	DE ST Center-entrance city
Bay State 4175	Laconia, 1914	Standard 0-50	DE DT Semi-convertible
(Later Coast Cities Railway [NJ] 703.)			
Eastern Mass. 4387	Laconia, 1918	Bay State 12C	DE DT Semi-convertible
Brooklyn Rapid Transit 4547	Jewett, 1906	Baldwin 185-P25	DE DT Convertible
Boston ER 5055, 5060/71	Brill, 1906	Brill 27-E-2/27-BE2	DE DT Type 2 semi-convertible
Boston ER 5734	Brill, 1924	Standard C-35P	DE DT Type 5A1 lightweight semi-convertible
(On loan to Boston MBTA and since July 1995 displayed at Boylston Station.)			
Baltimore UR&E 5748 (originally 1504)	Brill, 1917	Brill 27-G-1	DE DT semi-convertible
Boston ER 5821	Brill, 1924	Standard C-35P	DE DT Type 5B lightweight semi-convertible

A. City and Suburban Cars, *continued*

Boston ER 6131	Kuhlman, 1919	Taylor RH	DE DT Center-entrance city
Baltimore UR&E 6144	Brill, 1930	Brill 177E-1X	SE DT Lightweight "Peter Witt" city
Boston ER 6270	Kuhlman, 1918	Brill 77E-1	DE DT Center-entrance city
(This car is in poor condition and may not be restored.)			
Boston ER 6309	Laconia, 1921,	Taylor RH	DE DT Center-entrance city
Philadelphia PTC 6618	Brill, 1912	Brill 39-E	SE DT "Nearside" city
Eastern Mass. St. Railway 7005	Osgood-Bradley, 1927	Brill 177-E-1X	DE DT Lightweight city
(Later Boston MBTA 4400.)			

Philadelphia SEPTA (P&W) "Bullet" 207, Boston MBTA PCCs 3037/69/99/122/174, and Boston ex-Dallas PCCs 3328/31/38/44 (Dallas 623, 610, 603 and 611) are owned but not accessioned. They store parts and continue to be maintained. Boston 3338 was once (fictitious) New Bedford (MA) 701. Templeton Street Railway 24 (Briggs 1901) was a body in poor condition and was scrapped many years ago. Montreal austerity city cars 1176/77 (home-built, 1943) were scrapped for parts. Connecticut Co. 15-bench open 1253 was destroyed by spontaneous combustion in the 1940s, when sunlight hit its magnifying headlight lens.

B. Interurban and Electric Freight Cars

Mousam River RR	Portland, 1893	Unknown	DE ST Mail and baggage trailer
(Later Atlantic shore line car, later York Utilities 8.)			
Portland-Lewiston (ME) 14	Laconia, 1912	Baldwin A	DE DT Interurban coach "Narcissus"
Kansas City, Clay Co. & St. Joseph Ry. 24	Cincinnati, 1913	–	DT DE Center-entrance interurban coach (body only)
Chicago, South Shore & South Bend 32	Standard, 1929	Baldwin 84-60AA	DE DT Interurban coach
Southwest Missouri RR 39	Home-built, 1913	Taylor TA-70MCB	DE DT Interurban coach
Aroostook Valley (ME) 52	Brill, 1909	Brill 27-E-1	DE DT Express motor
Aroostook Valley (ME) 70/71	Wason, 1912	Brill 27-MCB-2	DE DT Combine
Portsmouth, Dover & York (NH, ME) 108	Laconia, 1904	Standard C-50	DE DT Express/Mail car
Rochester & Sodus Bay 113	Jackson & Sharp, 1899	–	DE DT Interurban coach (body only)
Cedar Rapids & Iowa City Ry. 118	Cincinnati, 1930	Cincinnati ABC74D	SE DT Lightweight interurban coach
(Originally Cincinnati & Lake Erie 118.)			
Boston & Worcester St. Ry. 149	Unknown	–	DE DT Interurban coach
(This car was modernized in the 1920s and given the name "City of Boston.")			
Lake Shore Electric (OH) 171	Jewett, 1918	Baldwin 84-45	DE DT Interurban coach
Chicago, North Shore & Milwaukee 415	Cincinnati, 1926	Baldwin 84-30AA	DE DT Interurban dining car
Chicago, North Shore & Milwaukee 420	Pullman, 1928	Baldwin 84-30AA	DE DT Interurban coach
Chicago, Aurora & Elgin 434	Cincinnati, 1927	Baldwin 84-30AA	DE DT Interurban coach
Quebec Ry. Lt. & Power 454	Ottawa, 1930	Brill 27-MCB	SE DT Interurban coach
Montreal & So. Co. 504	Ottawa, 1924	Taylor 6' MCB	SE DT Express motor
Montreal & So. Co. 610	Ottawa, 1922	Taylor 6' MCB	SE DT Interurban coach
Montreal & So. Co. 621	Ottawa, 1930	Baldwin 6' 6"	DE DT Interurban coach
Originally Windsor, Essex & Lake Shore Railway [ON] 501.)			
Cincinnati & Lake Erie 648	Cincinnati, 1930	Taylor MCB	DE DT Express motor
(Later Tulsa-Sapulpa Union Railway [OK] 202.)			
Chicago, N. Shore & Milwaukee 755	Standard, 1930	Baldwin 84-30AA	DE DT Interurban coach
Lake Erie & Northern (ON) 797	Preston, 1915	Baldwin MCB	DE DT Combine
Lehigh Valley (PA) 1030	ACF, 1931	Cincinnati ABC74D	SE DT Lightweight interurban parlor car
(Originally Indiana RR 55.)			
Rhode Island 1280	Home-built, 1912	Taylor MCB	DE DT Express/baggage car
British Columbia El. Ry. 1304	Home-built, 1946	Unknown	DE DT Interurban coach
(On loan to Oregon Electric Railway Historical Society, now at the new Brooks OR site.)			
Berkshire Street Railway (Pittsfield, MA)	Wason, 1903	–	DE DT Parlor car "Berkshire Hills" (body only)

C. Rapid Transit Cars

U.S. Dept. of Trnsptn. 1, 2	Boeing Vertol/ St. Louis, 1972	General Steel 70	SE DT "State of the art" subway
Budapest (Hungary) 18	Siemens-Halske/ Schlick'sche, 1896	Unknown	DE DT Center-entrance "Foldalatti" subway
Boston MBTA 0210	Pressed Steel, 1906	Standard C-60	DE DT Elevated
(Converted to wrecker-tool car in 1939.)			
New York, Staten Island RT 366	Standard, 1925	Unknown	DE DT Rapid transit
Boston MBTA 0512/13	Pullman, 1923	Taylor TR	SE DT Rapid transit
Boston MBTA 0546/47	Pullman, 1924	Taylor TR	SE DT Rapid transit
Boston MBTA 0559/62	St. Louis, 1951	General Steel	SE DT PCC Rapid transit
Boston MBTA 0719/24/53	Osgood-Bradley, 1927	Brill 27-MCB-2/3	DE DT Rapid transit
New York IND 800	ACF, 1936	CF 506 AB	DE DT Type R-9 subway
Boston MBTA 0997, 01000	Wason, 1928	Standard C-60	DE DT Rapid transit
Philadelphia SEPTA 1018	Brill, 1936	Commonwealth	DE DT "Bridge" subway
Phila., Delaware River Bridge Commsn. 1023	Brill, 1936	Commonwealth	DE DT "Bridge" subway
Boston MBTA 01158/59	Pullman-Standard, 1957	General Steel 70	SE DT Modified PCC rapid transit
New York IND 1440	ACF, 1936	ACF 75 AB	DE DT Type R-7A subway
Boston MBTA 01450/55	Pullman-Standard, 1963	General Steel 70	SE DT Rapid transit
New York IRT 3352	ACF, 1905	Baldwin MCB	DE DT High-V "Gibbs" subway
Long Island RR 4137	ACF, 1930	12D8P1/2CP3	DE DT Type MP-54A1 MU Commuter
Chicago CTA 6599/600	St. Louis, 1957	St. Louis B-3	SE DT PCC Rapid transit

A set of Clark B-10 PCC trucks from Boston 1951 rapid transit cars is in store for possible use. New York subway car (NYCTA) 175 (ACF, 1932) and Boston rapid transit cars 0709/49/54 are owned but not accessioned, being used as a parts source and for storage. New York Interborough 890 (Gilbert, 1887), stored in California for Seashore, was destroyed by fire in May, 1994.

D. Work Cars and Locomotives

Ottawa TC B-2	Ottawa, 1926	Unknown	DE ST Snow sweeper
(Later Cornwall Street Railway 2.)			
Claremont (NH) 4	Unknown	Standard C35P	DE ST Line car
Providence (RI) UER 16	Wason, 1905	Wason	DE ST Snow plow
Eastern Mass. S-71	Home-built (Bay State), 1915	Peckham	DE ST Line car
Atlantic Shore Line (York, ME) 100	Laconia, 1906	Alco	DE DT Steeple cab locomotive
Groton & Stonington 106	Unknown	–	DE DT Wedge plow (body only)
Oshawa (ON) 300	Baldwin, 1920	Baldwin MCB	DE ST Steeple cab locomotive
Connecticut Co. 0357	McGuire-Cummings, 1925	Wason AB	DE DT Unmotored flat
Boston MBTA 0503	Home-built, 1901	Standard C-60	DE DT Subway flat
Boston MBTA 0504	Industrial, 1901	Baldwin MCB	DE DT Subway crane
Boston MBTA 0514	Home-built 1914	Baldwin	DE DT Subway yard locomotive
Boston MBTA 0517	Goldschmidt, 1913	Angle iron	DE ST rail grinder
Boston MBTA 0521	Brill, 1916	Standard C-60	DE DT Subway box motor with crane
Boston MBTA 0551	Industrial, 1911	Standard C-60	DE DT Subway crane
Boston MBTA 0553	Russell, 1916	Brill 27-MCB-2	DE DT Subway wrecker/tool car
Boston MBTA 0576	Unknown, 1924	Taylor TR	DE DT Subway motorized flat car with crane
Eastern Mass. P-601	Russell, 1920	Standard C-50	DE DT Snow sweeper
(Later New York TARS 86, became Toronto TTC S-31 in 1947.)			
Boston MBTA 1484	Home-built, 1925	Brill 21-E	DE ST trailer (formerly a pump car)
Boston MBTA 2003	Home-built, 1910	Standard 0-50	DE DT Motor flat
Boston MBTA 2016	Home-built, 1912	Standard 0-50	DE DT Motor flat with hoist
Boston MBTA 2026	Home-built, 1910	Standard C-60	DE DT Motor flat with hoist
Boston MBTA 3234	Goldschmidt, 1913	Angle Iron	DE ST Rail grinder
Boston MBTA 3246	Industrial, 1916	Industrial	DE DT 10 ton crane
Boston MBTA 3266	Home-built, 1919	Unknown	DE ST Unmotored paint storage car (body only)
Boston MBTA 3603	Home-built, 1923	Unknown	SE ST Ramp flat
Boston MBTA 3608	Differential, 1926	Taylor HLB	DE DT Side dump

Boston MBTA 3617	Differential, 1927	Standard C-50	DE DT Bottom dump
(On loan to Boston MBTA as 2617.)			
Boston MBTA 3622	Differential, 1927	Taylor TR	DE DT Side dump
Boston MBTA 5154/59	St. Louis, 1908	Standard C-50	DE DT Type 3 semi-convertible plow

(5154 will be restored as a Type 3 passenger car, 5159 as a Type 3 plow.)

Philadelphia SEPTA (Red Arrow) snow sweeper 5 (Russell, 1918) and Boston MBTA flatcars 0507/54 (not accessioned) are service and tool cars. No. 5 once owned by Empire State RR, was later New York State Rys. 3014 (Syracuse). Worcester (MA) 038 Motor flat is disassembled for possible restoration. Boston MBTA type 3 semi-convertible plows 5106/22 (St. Louis, 1908, Standard C-50 trucks) are not accessioned and are used as utility cars.

E. Electric Trolley Buses

BUS	BUILDER AND DATE	SERIAL NUMBER
Shreveport (LA) 105/06	Brill T30S, 1931/32	–
Halifax (NS) 273	CCF-Brill T44A, 1950	6735
Philadelphia SEPTA 336	Marmon-Herrington TC49, 1955	15502
Dayton CTC 376	Pullman-Standard, 1942	–
Seattle Metro 627 (originally 867)	Twin Coach 41GWFT, 1940	75201
Wilmington, Delaware Elect. Pwr. 623	Brill 40SMT, 1939	489
(Owned by Rockhill Trolley Museum, Orbisonia [PA] until 1996.)		
Wilmington, Delaware Elect. Pwr. 654	Mack CR3S, 1940	1222
Johnstown (PA) Transit Co. 713	Brill 40SMT, 194	688
(Originally Wilmington, Delaware Electric Power 664.)		
Cleveland CTS 1052	St. Louis, 1947	–
Boston MTA 8361	Pullman-Standard 450S-102-43CX, 1948	–
Boston MTA 8490	Pullman-Standard 44CX, 1951	–

F. Motor Buses

Biddeford & Saco Bus lines 31	ACF-Brill C-36, 1947	620 (Gasoline)
(Originally Lynnefield (MA) Community bus lines 34, later 25.)		
St. Clairesville (OH)	Twin Coach 23S, 1934	– (Gasoline)
Red Star Way Lines A-60		
New York Surface Transport 87	Mack CM4D, 1942	1178 (Diesel-electric)
(Later U.S. Navy (CA) 32792.)		
Massachusetts Ntheastn. St. Ry. 116	ACF P-85, 1929 "Nancy Hanks"	– (Gasoline)
Middlesex & Boston St. Ry. 192	ACF-Brill C-36, 1948	345 (Gasoline)
Eastern Massachusetts St. Ry. 478	ACF H-9-S, 1934	58 (Gasoline)
Portland (ME) 504 (originally PE 2819)	GM TDH-5103, 1950	120 (Diesel)
Eastern Massachusetts St. Ry. 523	Twin Coach Model 40, 1934	– (Gasoline)
Brantford (ON) 627	GM TGH-3102, 1962	452 (Gasoline)
Boston MTA 788	Mack C-41 GT, 1947	1534 (Gasoline)
Boston ER 964	Twin Coach Model 40, 1932	– (Gasoline)
Boston MTA 1508	White 788, 1946	321641 (Gasoline)
London Transport (UK) RTL 162	Leyland/Weymann, 1954	– (Diesel double-deck)
Boston MTA 2824	White Model 788, 1948	341446 (Gasoline)
Boston MTA 2918	White 1144, 1951	384891 (Gasoline)
Eastern Massachusetts St. Ry. 3524	GM TDH-5302, 1961	471 (Diesel)
(Later Boston MBTA 3524.)		
Boston MBTA 6169	GMC TDH-5303, 1967	– (Diesel)
Providence (RI), United Elec. Ry. 7217	Twin Coach 44D, 1947	184 (Gasoline)
Boston MBTA 9138	Flyer Industries D901, 1982	– (Diesel)
Wayland (MA) Public Schools (Natick)	Graham, 1924	– (Gasoline)
Williamsport (PA) unidentified	Yellow Coach Model 717, 1934	– (Gasoline)
Unidentified	Ford 69B, 1946	– (Gasoline)

MARYLAND

Baltimore

1. ***Baltimore Streetcar Museum,*** *PO Box 4881, Baltimore, MD 21211-0881. (410) 547-0264. 5' 4 1/2" gauge trolley museum at 1901 Falls Road Baltimore. Cars run Sundays all year noon-5:00 p.m., Saturdays and holidays Memorial Day to end of October noon-5:00 p.m.*

At the BSM's heart is a group of cars collected by Baltimore's United Railways & Electric Company in the 1920s. The successor Baltimore Transit Company donated them in 1954 to a group planning a museum near Lake Roland. When that site proved impractical, the group split. One segment, which later became the National Capital Trolley Museum, in 1966 took its cars closer to Washington. The other incorporated as the BSM. Encouraged and assisted by the city, the BSM moved to the Falls Road site and ran its first car on what is officially Baltimore's route 25 on July 3, 1970. Unhappily, the site is flood-prone and hurricane-related inundations have caused damage over the years, although it has always been made good. The BSM, now actively looking to relocate, recently became a member of the Inner Harbor Streetcar Preservation Trust, which is proposing several tourist trolley lines including one linking the Inner Harbor and the Baltimore & Ohio RR museum. However, BSM relocation in no way hinges on completion of the Inner Harbor project.

A. City and Suburban Cars

CAR	BUILDER AND DATE	TRUCKS	CAR TYPE
Baltimore CPR 25	Poole & Hunt 1859	Pedestal	DE ST Horse car (body only)
Baltimore CPR 129	Home-built, 1879	Pedestal	DE ST Horse car
Newport News (VA) 90 (later 390)	Brill, 1918	–	DE DT Semi-convertible city (body only)

(Ten of this fifty car order for Newport News were diverted to Baltimore. This car, from the same batch, will be restored as Baltimore 5885, as if it had been the eleventh car diverted to Baltimore. The car will be loaned to the Inner Harbor project)

Baltimore UR&E 264	Brownell, 1900	Lord Baltimore Max. Traction	DE DT Convertible

(Originally numbered 814, became 1814 in 1905, 1944 in 1907, and 264 in 1917.)

Baltimore CPR 417	Home-built, circa 1888-91	Lord Baltimore	DE ST City ex-horse car

(Became electric car 427 in 1896, 417 in 1897, 2302 in 1899, shop utility car 6024 in 1910.)

Baltimore BT 554	Brownell, 1896	Lord Baltimore	DE ST 9-bench open

(Became 164 in 1899, 1264 in 1911, snow scraper 3390 in 1925.)

Baltimore CPR 1050	Brownell, 1898	Lord Baltimore	DE ST City

(Became 2135 in 1902, 390 in 1910, 396 in 1912, 2801 in 1917, trailer pusher 3651 in 1925.)

Baltimore UR&E 1164	Brill, 1902	Brill 22-E	DE DT 12-bench open

(Originally numbered 2458, became 1164 in 1906.)

Baltimore UR&E 3828	Brill, 1902	Brill 22-E	DE DT City

(Originally numbered 1028, became 3828 in 1923.)

Baltimore UR&E 4533	Brill, 1904	Brill 21-E	DE ST City

(Originally numbered 1306, became 447 in 1906, 2306 in 1914, 3407 in 1920, rebuilt in 1924 with safety car features and numbered 4533, became rail bond test car 3550 in 1933.)

Baltimore UR&E 4662	Brill, 1904	Brill 21-E	DE ST City

(Originally numbered 1615, became 115 in 1905, 464 in 1910, 2324 in 1914, 929 in 1920, 2709 in 1922 and 4662 in 1925.)

Baltimore UR&E 6119	Brill, 1930	Brill 177-E-1X	SE DT Lightweight "Peter Witt" city
Baltimore UR&E 7059	Brill, 1920	–	DE DT Trailer (body only)

(This car is to be loaned to the Inner Harbor project.)

Baltimore BTC 7350	Pullman, 1940	–	SE DT PCC (body only)
Baltimore BTC 7407	Pullman, 1944	Clark B-2	SE DT PCC
Baltimore UR&E 8639	(Brill, 1902)	–	DE DT 12-bench open (body only)

(Originally numbered 1089 as a 12-bench open, became 1139 in 1918. Rebuilt 1925 as one unit of a two-unit permanently-coupled train and numbered 8639. This car body has one side missing but is to be loaned to the Inner Harbor project and rebuilt.)

Baltimore PCC 7329 (Pullman, 1939) was scrapped for parts by the BSM. The body of Baltimore PCC 7350 (Pullman, 1940) exists in the area but is not owned by the BSM. A full-size replica model of a Baltimore PCC, mounted on rubber tires and built for the Barry Levinson Levinson movie *Avalon,* is now part of the BSM collection.

B. Electric Trolley Buses

BUS	BUILDER AND DATE	SERIAL NUMBER
Baltimore UR&E 4802	Brill Rail-less, 1922	(body only)
Baltimore BTC 2078	Pullman-Standard 44CX, 1940	–

C. Motor Buses

Baltimore BTC 1096	GMC TDH-4506, 1945	001 (Diesel)
Baltimore BTC 1962	GMC TDH-5303, 1963	– (Diesel)

2. ***Inner Harbor Streetcar Preservation Trust,*** *PO Box 27161, Baltimore, MD 21230.*

The Inner Harbor Streetcar Preservation Trust is acting on several proposals to link Baltimore's Inner Harbor with the Baltimore & Ohio RR Museum by tourist trolley. The Baltimore Streetcar Museum is a member of the Trust and will move to a site near the B&O RR museum if the line goes in. Parts from three Boston MBTA subway cars (Pullman, 1923/4), including three pairs of Taylor trucks, were bought by the Baltimore Streetcar Museum to restore cars for the Inner Harbor project.

Myersville

Don Easterday, *Canada Hill Road, Myersville, MD 21773. (301) 293-2888. Private collection, not open to the public.*

When Don Easterday learned that former Hagerstown and Frederick Railway right-of-way ran through his property it sparked a desire to locate, buy and restore a car from the line. The restoration of H&F 150 is the result. Built for the U. S. Army in 1918, it was sold to the H&F in 1923 and ran until 1938. It is kept in outdoor storage on Easterday's property. Profits from the Harwood book "Blue Ridge Trolley" help maintain it. Other cars in the area include Frederick city car 62, recently offered by the city of Frederick to Don Easterday, and H&F combine 168, being restored by the Hagerstown Roundhouse Museum.

Wheaton

National Capital Historical Museum of Transportation (National Capital Trolley Museum), *PO Box 4007, Silver Spring, MD 20914-0007. (301) 384-6088. Standard-gauge trolley museum at Bonifant Road, between Layhill Road and New Hampshire Avenue, north of Wheaton MD. Cars run weekends all year noon-5:00 p.m. Wednesdays in July and August, weekends in December 5:00 p.m.-9:00 p.m.*

The NCTM collects cars of Washington D. C., Maryland and Pennsylvania, plus European cars to compare practices and techniques. The NCTM and the Baltimore Streetcar Museum have common roots but split in 1966. The Lake Roland site in Baltimore was vandal-prone, while a proposed Montgomery County site was too distant for the Baltimore people. The NCTM began in 1970 at the present site, Northwest Branch Park in Montgomery County, leased from Maryland's National Capital Park and Planning Commission. The M-NCPPC is seeking ISTEA funds to build a new museum in the park, partly because portions of the present site are in a 100-year flood plain of Northwest Branch and partly to change the museum's emphasis from rides to a more comprehensive "museum experience."

A. City & Suburban Cars

CAR	BUILDER AND DATE	TRUCKS	CAR TYPE
Graz (Austria) 120	Grazer Waggonfabrik, 1909	Unknown	DE ST City
(Originally Grazer Tramway Gesellschaft 88, became Grazer Verkehrsbetriebe 120 in 1953/54 when rebuilt to present condition.)			
Johnstown Traction Co. 352	St. Louis, 1926	St. Louis EDJ 64	DE DT Lightweight city
Capital Traction (DC) 522	American, 1898	Brill 21-E	DE ST City
New York TARS 678	TARS, 1939	Brill 77-E	DE DT Lightweight city
(Later Vienna, [Austria] Type Z 4220 {Wiener Stadtwerke Verkehrsbetriebe.)			
DC Transit 766	Kuhlman, 1918	Brill 77-E-1	DE DT City
Rhine Ry. Co. Dusseldorf (Germany) 955	Gebruder Schondorff, 1928	Unknown	DE ST City
(Rheinische Bahngesellschaft AG 955. Became Karlsruhe 955 in 1966.)			
DC Transit 1053	St. Louis, 1935	St. Louis Capital 70	SE DT pre-PCC
DC Transit 1101	St. Louis, 1937	Clark B-2	DE ST PCC
DC Transit 1540	St. Louis, 1945	–	DE ST PCC (body only)
(Later Fort Worth 6 [1]. A set of Clark B-2 trucks is available for this car's restoration.)			
Toronto TTC 4603	St. Louis/CCF, 1951	Clark B-2	SE DT Type A-15 PCC
(Originally Toronto TTC Type A-8 4548.)			
Berlin (Germany) 5954	Unknown, 1924/5	Unknown	DE ST Type T24 city
(Berliner Verkehrsbetriebe 5954. Became Karlsruhe 5954 in 1967.)			

Vienna (Austria) 6062	Simmeringer Waggonfabrik, 1910	Unknown	DE ST City

(Wiener Stadtwerke-Verkehrsbetriebe. Originally Type H passenger car 2249, type H1 in 1935, type HP snow plow 6062 in 1962.)

Vienna (Austria) 7802	Waggonfabrik Stauding, 1910	Unknown	DE ST Trailer

(Wiener Stadtwerke-Verkehrsbetriebe Type K1 trailer 3386, renumbered Type KP 7802 in 1966.)

DC Transit air-conditioned PCC 1512 (St. Louis, 1945), was destroyed in a 1970 arson attack. Its trucks will be used under PCC 1540. Cleveland RTA (Shaker) PCC car 75 (Pullman-Standard, 1947), stored at Trolleyville USA, Olmstead Falls OH, was sold to NCTM in 1996 for parts. Its Clark B-2 trucks are under TTC 4603, the electrical equipment may be used on DC Transit 1540.

B. Work Cars and Locomotives

DC Transit 07	McGuire, 1899	McGuire	DE ST Snow sweeper

(Originally Washington Traction & Electric Car.)

DC Transit 026	Brill, 1905	Brill Pedestal	DE ST Snow sweeper

(Originally Washington, Alexandria & Mt. Vernon Ry. Co. 51, later Capital Transit Co. 026.)

DC Transit 0509	American, 1899	Peckham 14B	DE DT work car

MASSACHUSETTS

Boston

1. **Boston Street Railway Association,** *PO Box 181037, Boston, MA 02118-1037. (617) 433-7015.*

The BSRA was founded in 1959 "to publish, exhibit and preserve materials and information on local and regional mass transit." It owns Boston MTA Type 5A1 No. 5706, (Brill, 1924, Standard C-35P trucks) which is at the Shore Line Trolley Museum, but it is not restored and not displayed. The BSRA magazine "Rollsign" is published every two months.

2. **Massachusetts Bay Transportation Authority,** *10 Park Plaza, Boston, MA 02116. (617) 722-5000. Standard-gauge PCC and heritage cars.*

The MBTA is Boston's mass transit provider, with a dense network of commuter rail, rapid transit, light rail, ETB and motor bus lines. The Ashmont-Mattapan line's PCC cars, although heavily rebuilt some years ago, are at the end of their useful life. Options include rebuilding the PCCs again ($1 million per car), replacing them with Boeing LRVs, rebuilding the line's bridges and power supply, extending the Red Line rapid transit from Ashmont to Mattapan, or replacing the line altogether, possibly with a guided busway.

A. MBTA PCCs still in service on Ashmont-Mattapan line.

3087, 3230/32/34/38/54/60/62/63/65/68. Pullman-Standard 1944 (3087), 1945 (remainder), Clark B-2 trucks SE DT MU PCC cars.

B. Other MBTA heritage cars

PCCs 3222/41/64 (Pullman-Standard, 1945) stored. PCC 3295 (Pullman-Standard, 1951) is kept as a museum piece in 1959 colors. Type 5 semi-convertible 5734 is leased from the Seashore Trolley Museum. Since July 1995, 3295 and 5734 have been displayed at Boylston Station.

C. MBTA Work and maintenance of way cars built prior to 1953.

CAR	BUILDER AND DATE	TRUCKS	CAR TYPE
2617	Differential, 1927	Standard C-50	DE DT Bottom dump car
(Originally 3617, on loan from Seashore Trolley Museum.)			
2626	Differential, 1925	Taylor	DE DT Side dump car
(Formerly 3626, this car was heavily rebuilt in 1985.)			
3283	Henry Dow, 1950	Unknown	DE DT Wire car
3327	Pullman-Standard, 1945	Clark B-2	DE DT PCC Maintenance of way car

(Originally Dallas Railway & Terminal 622.)

| 3332 | Pullman-Standard, 1945 | Clark B-2 | DE DT PCC Wire car |
| | | | |

(Originally Dallas Railway & Terminal 618, later a Boston sand car.)

| 3343 | Pullman-Standard, 1945 | Clark B-2 | DE DT PCC Rerailer |

(Originally Dallas Railway & Terminal 613.)

| 5138/64 | St. Louis, 1907 | Standard C-50 | DE DT Type 3 Snow plow |

(Converted from Type 3 semi-convertible, 1928, 1927.)

Lowell

Lowell National Historical Park, 67 Kirk Street, Lowell, MA 01852. (508) 970-5000. Standard-gauge tourist trolley. Board cars at Boott Mill or Vistors center. Cars run daily March-November, except during Lowell Folk Festival, usually the last weekend of July.

Lowell is the cradle of American industry. Water power was first used here for textile manufacture and by 1900 Lowell was America's No. 1 textile-making town. It was all gone by 1970. Abandoned mills, canals and railroad lines of the old Lowell were part of a well-defined, largely-intact area with shops, churches and houses. This attracted the National Park Service, wanting to create an urban industrial heritage park to preserve and interpret 19th and early 20th century factory manufacturing. They set up the LNHP in 1978 to do exactly that in Lowell. Missing, as they saw it, was local transport and in their focus period, that meant trolleys. Since May 26, 1984, replicas of Lowell cars 1597-1600 (Brill, 1902) move visitors between the exhibits on several routes, none more than a mile long. The most intensively served is that from Boott Mill to the Visitor's Center alongside the Merrimack canal. There is talk of more replica cars plus an extension to connect the system with the MBTA commuter rail station and other city attractions.

CAR	BUILDER AND DATE	TRUCK	CAR TYPE
Lowell 1601/02	Gomaco, 1983	Melbourne type 1	DE DT Replica 15-bench open
Lowell 4131	Gomaco, 1987	Melbourne type 1	DE DT Semi-convertible

(Replica of a 1912 St. Louis-built car for the Bay State Street Railway [MA], which operated in Lowell.)

Shelburne Falls

Shelburne Falls Trolley Museum, 12 Water Street, Shelburne Falls, MA 01370.

Established in 1992, the SFTM is building a museum centered on the restored body of Shelburne Falls and Coleraine Street Railway combine 10 (Wason, 1896), located at the foot of the 1908 trolley bridge crossing the Deerfield River to Buckland MA. This five-span concrete-arched "Bridge of Flowers" gave a direct link to the Boston & Maine and the New Haven Railroads at Buckland Station. In 1996, the SFTM received $200,000 in ISTEA money to begin the restoration and is now seeking matching funds to begin the work. The SFTM also collects, preserves, displays and interprets railroad and trolley artifacts and historical data from Western Massachusetts.

MICHIGAN

Dearborn

Henry Ford Museum, PO Box 1970, Dearborn, MI 48121. (313) 271-1620. Static streetcar display, steam passenger train runs around the grounds. Museum open 9:00 a.m.- 5:00 p.m. daily year-round except Thanksgiving, Christmas and New Year's Day.

The Henry Ford Museum is a world-class museum of Americana, part of the larger Greenfield Village outdoor museum complex and not to be missed by any visitor with a soft spot for American or transportation history.

CAR	BUILDER AND DATE	TRUCK	CAR TYPE
New York (Hunter's Point & Erie Basin RY) 1	Jones, 1881	Pedestal	DE ST Horse car
Troy (NY) Lumber District Ry. 24	Unknown, circa 1885	Pedestal	DE ST Horse car
Fort Collins (CO) 26	American, 1924	Brill 79-E-1	DE ST Birney "safety"
Cleveland Electric Ry. 165	Brill, 1892	Brill 21-A	SE ST City

(Rebuilt in Company shops 1902 as wrecker 0140. May still be in this configuration.)

Detroit DSR 3865 (St. Louis, 1931) was to have been transferred to the MSR, San Francisco, in 1996 but the deal fell through.

Detroit

Detroit Citizens' Railway *(owned and operated by the Detroit Department of Transportation) 1301 East Warren, Detroit, MI 48207. Tourist trolley, 2' 11 7/16" gauge. Runs daily year-round on Washington Boulevard to Cobo Hall and Renaissance Center.*

This, the first new-start stand-alone tourist trolley line in North America, opened September 20, 1976, nearly two decades after Detroit's last streetcar ran. The mile-long line was to have been standard-gauge, using (among others) Brooklyn 4550, bought from the Edaville RR for the purpose. However, this was a Bicentennial project, 4550 could not be made ready for a 1976 opening, and the chance to buy operational Lisbon cars was too good to miss. Brooklyn 4550 was sold and by the mid-80s was at Pittsburgh's Station Square, where it remains. For some years cars ran every ten minutes, seven days a week. An extension from Cobo Hall to the Renaissance Center opened in 1980. But the area the line was to help revitalize fell on hard times, discouraging tourists and the 1987 opening of the elevated people-mover, serving the same general area, robbed the line of more riders. Funding became tight when state-sourced operating money was withdrawn and despite their excellent external appearance, years of deferred maintenance had left only one or two operable cars. In 1996, a determined effort was made to resume daily service.

CAR	BUILDER AND DATE	TRUCK	CAR TYPE
Detroit CR 1/2/3 (Lisbon 405/36/12)	St. Louis, 1900	Brill 21-E	DE ST City
Detroit CR 4 (Lisbon 517)	Home-built 1925	Brill 21-E	DE ST Semi-convertible
Detroit CR 5 (Lisbon 523)	Home-built 1925	Brill 21-E	DE ST Semi-convertible
Detroit CR 6 (Lisbon 427)	St. Louis, 1900	Brill 21-E	DE ST City
Vevy (Switzerland) 9 (Later Fribourg [Switzerland 5].)	Unknown	Unknown	DE ST City
Burton & Ashby Light Ry. (England) 14	Brush, 1904	Brill 21-E	DE ST Open-top double-deck city
Lisbon, Portugal 247 (later 397)	Brill, 1900	Brill 21-E	DE ST 8-bench open

Lisbon 457 and 529 were acquired for parts. Before deciding on narrow-gauge cars, the DCR acquired the body of Reading (PA) Transit & Light Birney 510 (Osgood-Bradley, 1920) in 1973 from the defunct Magee Transportation Museum at Bloomsburg PA. Toronto TTC Type A-8 PCC cars 4524 and 4529, plus Philadelphia SEPTA PCC cars 2092/98/2111/17/18/34/50/59, 2712/13/16/17/61/80 were acquired in 1996 by Dennis Ammerman, a Detroit businessman who has raised $5 million to install a standard-gauge tourist trolley from Grand Circus Park via Woodward to Detroit's Amtrak station. He has applied to the FTA for further money to begin the project.

Mount Clemens

Michigan Transit Museum, *PO Box 12, Fraser, MI 48026. (810) 463-1863. Standard-gauge rail museum, electric cars towed by diesel locomotive. Museum at Selfridge Air Force Base, 3/4 mile north of Mt. Clemens. Schedule changes frequently.*

The MTM began in January 1973 to preserve the last surviving Detroit Street Railway work cars. The MTM was interested in a tourist trolley project on West Vernor in Detroit. This later became the Washington Avenue line. Later, a site at Addison Oaks Park was considered, but at this time the MTM approached Selfridge Air National Guard Base personnel about storing cars on their railroad. A deal was struck with Colonel Robert Stone (the base's Chief of Supply & Services and its unofficial historian) in 1976 and the cars were used soon after arriving at the base to transfer VIPs to an upcoming air show. The MTM has since then run its cars (powered by a diesel locomotive) on unwired trackage leased from the Selfridge ANG base, 20 miles north of Detroit. In 1995, the base gave up its railroad, donating track and equipment to the MTM, in return for which MTM continues to provide VIP rail transport for the base's annual air show. The base also houses the Selfridge Military Air Museum (another of Colonel Stone's projects), which opened in 1981. The MTM leases the Grand Trunk RR station at Cass Avenue, Mount Clemens, MI., operating it as a museum. The present whereabouts of the DSR work cars that sparked the MTM's creation is unknown.

CAR	BUILDER AND DATE	TRUCK	CAR TYPE
Detroit SR 268	St. Louis, 1949	Clark B-2	SE DT PCC
(later Mexico City 2268)			
Chicago, North Shore &	Standard, 1929	Baldwin 84-30AA	DE DT Interurban coach
Milwaukee 761			
Chicago CTA 4442/50	Cincinnati, 1924	Baldwin 78-30	DE DT Elevated
Toronto TTC 4601 II	St. Louis/CCF, 1951	Clark B-2	SE DT Type A-15 PCC
(Originally Toronto TTC Type A-8 PCC 4512.)			

MINNESOTA

Chisholm

Ironworld USA, PO Box 392, Chisholm, MN 55719. Standard-gauge tourist trolley. Cars run daily May to September.

Ironworld tells the story of the Mesabe range, iron ore and the people who mined, processed and shipped it across America. The trolley provides internal transport and opened with the park on July 3, 1986. Cars are Melbourne M&MTB Type W2 601 and 606 (home-built, 1930), on M&MTB Type 1 trucks. The park also owns a Mesabe (MN) Transportation White bus built in 1916.

Duluth

Lake Superior Museum of Transportation, 506 W. Michigan Street, Duluth MN 55802. (218) 727-0687. Tourist trolley, 2' 11 7/16" gauge. Museum open daily 10 a.m.- 5:00 p.m.

A fine static display of restored upper-Midwest railrodiana housed in the beautifully refurbished Duluth Union Depot, plus a 1/4-mile segment of electrified trackage from the train shed into the yards, which began running in 1983. A 2 1/2-mile tourist trolley from downtown Duluth to the Amtrak station was originally planned and a 1985 study by Raymond Kaiser engineers recommended a four-mile extension of the station trolley line. Nothing was done and the museum's excursion business is handled by trains operating tourist service from southwestern Duluth to New Duluth alongside the St. Louis river on former Lake Superior and Mississippi Railroad tracks. The cars are Lisbon (Portugal) 530 and 531 (DE ST semi-convertible, home-built, 1925) on Brill 21-E swing-link trucks.

Minneapolis

Como-Harriet streetcar line, owned and operated by Minnesota Transportation Museum, PO Box 17240, Minneapolis, MN 55417. (612) 228-0263. Steamboat tickets (612) 474-4801. Standard-gauge trolley museum 6:30 p.m.- dusk weekdays Memorial Day weekend to Labor Day, 12.30 p.m -dusk weekends and holidays May-October. Board cars at Linden Hills Depot, 42nd and Queen Avenue South.

One of several divisions of the Minnesota Transportation Museum, the Como-Harriet line revives street railway trackage closed in 1954. With the survival of TCRT 1300 in working order, an embryonic museum group formed in 1962 and experimentally ran the car with a gasoline generator in back. Negotiations with the city's Park and Recreation Board led to the use of the present mile of old streetcar right-of-way. Runs over the first segment (still with generator in tow) began August 28, 1971 and under wire in 1973. The car house is being enlarged to accomodate PCC cars now stored at the former Jackson Street Roundhouse. The Linden Hills Depot is a shelter and an exhibit in its own right, being a recreation of the original depot, built on this site in 1900.

The streetcar steamboat Minnehaha, home-built in 1906 and under restoration for years, was successfully launched August 21, 1995. Between 1906 and 1926 an armada of TCRT steamboats sailed scheduled routes on Lake Minnetonka from May to September, linking lakeside parks, hotels, trolley and railroad terminii. Sea trials and fitting out of the revived Minnehaha continued until its maiden voyage on May 25, 1996 (accompanied by several MTM railroad division steam passenger specials and the bus division's 1399), after which it went into scheduled operation, serving Excelsior Dock, downtown Excelsior and Wayzata. Many 1996 sailings were completely sold out. Planned as an adjunct to the steamboat division is a separate streetcar line on which TCRT 1239 will ultimately be used. TCRT 1809 is used as a ticket and enquiry office at the new Excelsior steamboat dock.

A. City and Suburban Cars

CAR	BUILDER AND DATE	TRUCK	CAR TYPE
Duluth SR 78	Laclede, 1893	Brussels-built Brill 21-E	DE ST City
Duluth SR 265	TCRT, 1915	Baldwin modified trailer	SE DT City
(Originally TCRT 1791 {1}. Trucks from Chicago 4000-class trailers in which one motor has been fitted.)			
Twin Cities TCRT 322, 416	St. Louis, 1946	Clark B-2	SE DT PCC
(Became Newark TNJ 3, 27 in 1953, Cleveland RTA 3, 27 in 1977.)			
Twin Cities TCRT 1239	Home-built, 1908	–	SE DT Type H-6 city (body only)
Twin Cities TCRT 1300	Home-built, 1908	Baldwin 5	SE DT Type I-1 city
Twin Cities TCRT 1809	Home-built, 1917	–	DE DT Type L-8 city (body only)

B. Interurban Cars

Mesaba (MN) Electric Railway 10	Niles, 1912	–	SE DT Interurban coach (body only)

C. Rapid Transit Cars

Chicago CTA 4325/87	Cincinnati, 1922/1924	Baldwin 78-30	DE DT Elevated
(These cars were bought for parts. Car 4387 is now owned by John Larkin of Escanaba, WI.)			

D. Motor Buses

BUS	BUILDER AND DATE		SERIAL NUMBER
Twin Cities TCRT 103	GM TDH-5303, 1963		– (Diesel)
Twin Cities TCRT 630	Mack LD3G, 1942		1424 (Gasoline)
Twin Cities TCRT 1303	GM TDH-5105, 1954		– (Diesel)
Twin Cities TCRT 1399	GM TDH-5105, 1954		866 (Diesel)
Minneapolis MTC 1488	AM General, 197	– (Diesel)	

A 1937 TCRT Yellow Coach Model 733 was sold in 1996 to Old Pueblo Trolley of Tucson AZ for us in restoring a similar Tucson vehicle.

MISSOURI

Dearborn

The body of Kansas City, Clay County and St. Joseph Railway box motor 54 (owned by David Short and a loosely-knit group known as the Missouri Short line) is stored in Dearborn next to the town's original KC, CC and St. Joe depot which closed on the line's demise in 1933. It is to be used as a static display in a city park.

St. Louis

1. ***Museum of Transportation,*** *3015 Barrett Station Road, St. Louis, MO 63122. (314) 965-7998. Standard-gauge railroad and trolley museum. Open daily 9:00 a.m.-5:00 p.m. except Thanksgiving, Christmas and New Year's day.*

The MOT began as a successful 1944 project to save a St. Louis horse car. The present site was acquired in 1946. It was the first of the amateur-established museums to collect artifacts of all transportation modes. Its collection interest became national in the 1950s and for decades it was called the "National Museum of Transport." But too many exhibits competed for too few resources, ambitious plans came and went, yet in the early 1980s most exhibits were still in open storage. The St. Louis County Department of Parks and Recreation took over in 1983 after completing a five year lease and the original owners reorganized as a "Friends" (fundraising) group. For more than 50 years this was a static collection, but a short streetcar line has been built, the first tests were made in December 1996 and public operation may begin in 1997. A steam locomotive was successfully returned to operating condition in 1988 and a cosmetically-restored streetcar often graced MetroLink light rail construction ceremonies in the early 1990s.

A. City and Suburban Cars

CAR	BUILDER AND DATE	TRUCK	CAR TYPE
St. Louis Waterworks 10	St. Louis, 1914	Unknown	DE DT Suburban
St. Louis Waterworks 17	American, 1911	Unknown	DE DT Suburban
St. Louis, Bellefontaine 33	Brownell & White, 1880	Pedestal	SE ST Bobtail horse car
Illinois Terminal 104	American, 1924	Commonwealth 81	DE DT Center-entrance suburban
Philadelphia SEPTA (P&W) 204)	Brill, 1931	–	DE DT "Bullet" car (body only)
Illinois Terminal 410	St. Louis, 1924	St. Louis CM 69	DE DT Lightweight suburban
St. Louis PS 426	St. Louis, 1921	Commonwealth pedestal	SE DT Center-entrance trailer
St. Louis PS 615	St. Louis, 1902	URF 25	DT SE "Robertson sill" semi-convertible
(Originally St. Louis & Suburban 120, became 615 in 1911.)			
St. Louis PS 742	Home-built, 1921	Commonwealth cast steel	DT SE "Peter Witt" city
St. Louis PS 850	American, 1902	UR 25	DT DE City
(Originally St. Louis, St. Charles & Western 14, later UR 3009, later 850 (II). Body destroyed in 1980s by tunnel roof collapse at museum and only trucks and frame presently exist.)			
St. Louis PS 894	Laclede, 1896	UR 25	DE DT City
(Originally Southern Ry. (St. Louis) car, re-numbered 945, double-ended in 1913 and re-numbered 894, re-numbered 855 in 1939.)			
St. Louis PS 1001	Home-built, 1907	UR 25	SE DT City
St. Louis PS 1005 (originally 1065)	Home-built, 1909	UR 25	SE DT City (trailer puller)
Kansas City PS 1533	American, 1919	Brill 79-E-1	DE ST Birney "safety"
St. Louis PS 1664	St. Louis, 1941	Clark B-2	SE DT PCC
St. Louis PS 1743	St. Louis, 1946	Clark B-2	SE DT PCC
(Later San Francisco MUNI 1164)			
Philadelphia SEPTA 2186	St. Louis, 1948	Clark B-2 (ex-Chicago)	SE DT PCC
St. Louis PS 2250	St. Louis, 1903	UR 25	SE DT city
(This car is currently dismantled for restoration.)			
Philadelphia SEPTA 2740	St. Louis, 1947	Clark B-2 (ex-Chicago)	SE DT PCC

St. Louis PS city car 1031 (home-built, 1909) has been dismantled for parts. An unidentified double-end horsecar, claimed to be St. Louis, Union Depot Railway 3 (St. Louis, 1880), is part of the collection. Its pedigree is doubtful as it is of 3'6" gauge and not 4' 10 1/4" St. Louis gauge. It was returned to the St. Louis Car Company, displayed at the St. Louis Louisiana Purchase Exposition of 1904 and then stored at St. Louis Car until donated to the museum in 1948.

B. Interurban Cars

Purdue University test car 2611	Brill, 1903	Unknown	DE DT Interurban coach
(This car was used for testing at the 1904 Louisiana Purchase exposition, where it was an exhibit.)			
Illinois Terminal 203	White, 1939	–	Gasoline powered Railbus
Illinois Terminal 241	ACF, 1908	ACF 62	SE DT Combine

C. Rapid Transit Cars

New York PATH 256	Pressed Steel, 1909	Unknown	DE DT Subway
New York BMT 1365	Jewett, 1905	Unknown	DE DT Semi-convertible open-platform elevated
Chicago CTA 6711/12	St. Louis, 1959	St. Louis B-3	SE DT PCC rapid transit

D. Work Cars and Locomotives

St. Louis PS 60	Unknown, 1895	St. Louis 26	DE ST Weed-killer
(Originally St. Louis & Suburban sprinkler car, later St. Louis & Suburban water car 1010. Became weed-killer car in 1923.)			
St. Louis PS 76	Home-built, 1906	UR Diamond	DE DT Trailer flat
(Originally a line car built to haul a team and wagon, became trailer flat car in 1921.)			
St. Louis PS 77	Home-built, 1903	UR 25	DE DT Line car
(Originally refrigerator car "Z")			
St. Louis PS 165	Lindell Rlwy, 1893	Unknown	DE DT Wrecker
(Originally a Lindell Ry. (St. Louis) passenger car, became a wrecker in 1903.)			
St. Louis PS 215 (I)	Brownell, 1892	St. Louis 26	DE ST Rail Grinder
(Originally a passenger car, later a post office car, became rail grinder in 1910.)			
St. Louis PS 215 (II)	Home-built, 1945	St. Louis PS Special	DE ST Rail Grinder
Illinois Terminal 1575	Home-built, 1918	Alco RM-63B	DE DT Class B locomotive
Illinois Terminal 1595	Home-built, 1929	Alco RM-63B	DE four-truck Class C locomotive

E. Electric Trolley Buses

BUS	BUILDER AND DATE	SERIAL NUMBER
Fort Wayne 157	Brill 44SMT, 1942	299
Indianapolis Railways 527	Brill T40, 1934	–

F. Motor Buses

Enterprise, Scunthorpe (UK, EBE 259)	AEC Regent II, 1947	– (Diesel)
London Transport RT 8 (UK, FXT 183)	AEC/LT 2RT2, 1940	– (Diesel)
"Adolphus" for E. T. Strong of Buick	Yellow Coach Model 649, 1931	019 (Gasoline)
Toronto, Gray Coach Lines 41	Yellow Coach Model Y/TTC body, 1924	3037 (Gasoline)
Rogersville (MO)	Dodge/Superior, 1947	– (Gasoline school bus)
St. Louis PS instruction chassis	White, 1924	– (Gasoline)
St. Louis County Transit 21	Home-built, 1937	– (Gasoline)
St. Louis County Transit 97	Ford Model 69B, 1946	– (Gasoline)
New York City Omnibus 327	Yellow Coach Model 718, 1935	357 (Gasoline)
St. Louis PS 588	Yellow Coach Model Z, 1925	– (Gasoline)
(Originally People's Motor Bus, St. Louis.)		
Connecticut Co. 590	Yellow Coach 716, 1936	590 (Gasoline)
Indian Trails, Owosso MI 712	Yellow Coach Model 743, 1939	1256 (Gasoline)
(Originally a "Greyhound cruiser" bus, later Bee Line {Michigan} 512.)		
New York Fifth Ave. Coach 1234/35	Yellow Coach Model Z, 1930	135, 142 (Gasoline)
Omaha (NB) Transit 1315	Twin Coach 58D, 1950	16 Propane articulated)
New York City Omnibus 1592	Yellow Coach Model 731, 1936	126 (Gasoline)
New York Fifth Avenue Coach 2015	Yellow Coach Model 720, 1936	093 (Gasoline)
Paris (France) RATP 2052	Renault TN6 A2, 1932	– (Gasoline)
St. Louis PS 3529	Twin Coach Model 40, 1929	– (Gasoline)
St. Louis PS 4878	Yellow Coach TD 4006, 1940	039 (Diesel)
St. Louis Bi-State Dev. Agency 5065	AM General 9635A, 1975	066 (Diesel)
St. Louis Bi-State Dev. Agency 5359	AM General 9640A, 1975	060 (Diesel)
St. Louis Bi-State Dev Agency 7063	Flxible, 1977	62976 (Diesel)
Public Service New Jersey 8647	Yellow Coach Model 736, 1938	050 (Diesel-electric)

*2. **Old Spaghetti Factory Restaurant,** 707 North First Street St. Louis MO 63102. (314) 621-0276.*

The restaurant has Grand Forks (ND) Street Railway Birney "safety" car body 123 (St. Louis, 1920) as a dining-room centerpiece.

Webb City

Schifferdecker Park, Webb City, MO 64870. (417) 623-2341.

Two Southwest Missouri interurban cars are kept on city park property. One, powered by a diesel generator, operates on Labor Day weekend on railroad track in the park. A restored Southwest Missouri station and a memorial plaque to the system are also to be found in the park.

CAR	BUILDER AND DATE	TRUCK	CAR TYPE
Southwest Missouri ERR 5	Home-built, 1905	Unknown	DE DT Interurban coach
Southwest Missouri ERR	unidentified	American, 1927	DE DT Lightweight interurban coach (body only)

NEW JERSEY

Newark

NJ Transit, PO Box 10000, Newark, NJ 07101. (201) 643-7400. Standard-gauge heritage light rail. Cars run daily.

Newark's subway opened in 1935 on the abandoned Morris Canal's bed. Initially used by several routes, today's line 7 was by 1953 the sole survivor. PCC cars first ran in late-1953, older cars were retired by February 1954. Since 1957, line 7 has been the only trolley line in Greater New York and except for the Fort Worth (TX) subway with its exotically-bodied PCCs, is now the last

100% PCC operation in North America. An order for 45 low-floor cars was placed in 1996, 29 for the new Hudson-Bergen light rail line and sixteen for the Newark subway, which will be extended one mile to a new car house. They are expected by 1999.

A. City and Suburban Cars

CAR	BUILDER AND DATE	TRUCKS	CAR TYPE
1/2/4-7/9-17/19-26/28	St. Louis, 1946, 1947 (21-25), 1949 (26/28)		Clark B-2 SE DT PCC

(Originally TCRT (MN) RT 320/21/23-336/38/39/60-64/415/17. Cars 8/18/29/30 scrapped by 1985, 3 and 27 sold to Cleveland RTA (Shaker Heights) in 1977, now at Minnesota Transportation Museum.)

B. Work Cars

CAR	BUILDER AND DATE	TRUCKS	CAR TYPE
TNJ 5221	Russell, 1912	Unknown	DE DT Utility and line car
TNJ 5223 (originally PSNJ 2683)	Home-built, 1917	Unknown	DE DT Utility and flat car
TNJ 5245	Home-built, 1921	Unknown	DE DT Snow plow
TNJ 5246	Russell, 1921	Unknown	DE DT Snow sweeper

(Originally Trenton & Mercer County (NJ) 51 or 31, New York TARS 82 in 1935, Toronto TTC S-39 in 1938, TNJ 5246 in 1973.)

Paramus

Motor Bus Society, PO Box 251, Paramus, NJ 06753.

Established in 1948 as the National Motor Bus Association, the MBS collects information on North America's bus industry past and present. Its magazine Motor Coach Age publishes major articles on bus history (including the streetcars which preceded them) and though the MBS preserves no vehicles itself, many of its individual members collect and own historic buses.

Rahway

North Jersey Electric Railway Historical Society, PO Box 1170 Rahway, NJ 07065. Private collection, not open to the public.

An historical association devoted to electric transportation history and education, with a newsletter covering historical and current events in New Jersey, the NJERHS is restoring New Jersey Consolidated Transport DE DT City car 2651 (home-built, 1917).

Ringoes

Black River & Western RR, PO Box 200 Ringoes, NJ 08551. (201) 782-9600. Standard-gauge tourist railroad.

After the closure of the Magee Transportation Museum of Bloomsburg PA in 1972, this tourist railroad took over the body of Danville and Bloomsburg Street Railway car 1 (Brill, unknown date). The car is owned by a syndicate of several individuals.

NEW YORK

Buffalo

Niagara Frontier Transportation Authority, 181 Ellicott Street, Buffalo,NY 14203. (716) 855-7224. Standard-gauge light rail

In 1990, Buffalo's light rail and bus operator NFTA bought Cleveland RTA (Shaker Heights) PCC cars 51-55/60-62/67-70 (orginally TCRT 340-344/349-351/356-357/359-360, St. Louis, 1947) to use (refurbished) on the proposed Tonawanda branch. Originally to have split from the present light rail line at the underground La Salle Station, the 1991 plan envisaged a PCC-shuttle from a surface interchange at La Salle station traversing former railroad right-of-way to the Tonawandas. This plan remains stalled for lack of funds. Car 70 ran on Buffalo Main Street's surface tracks in December 1990, but otherwise, the cars have been stored unused at NFTA's car house. NFTA also owns Buffalo bus 602 (Mack C49 DT, 1956, serial number 1030).

Kingston (Rondout Landing)

Trolley Museum of New York, PO Box 2291, Kingston, NY 12402. (914) 331-3399. Standard-gauge trolley museum at 89 East Strand, Kingston (Rondout Creek waterfront). Open weekends and holidays noon-5:00 p.m. Memorial Day-Columbus Day

Established in 1955, the museum came to Kingston in 1983 as part of the Urban Cultural Park project. Its 1 1/4-miles of unwired track runs from the foot of Broadway to Kingston Point via the museum, in an area being restored to 19th century appearance. The museum is at milepost 1 of the old Ulster and Delaware RR and a shop building and exhibit hall have been built on the foundations of the (long-gone) turn-of-the-century engine house. The building's upper level houses a visitors center with historical displays. Picture windows overlook the shop, where restoration of eight of the museum's trolleys can be witnessed. At present the only operational vehicle is a 1929 Brill Model 55 gas-electric railroad passenger car (formerly a Sperry rail car).

A. City and Suburban Cars

CAR	BUILDER AND DATE	TRUCK	CAR TYPE
Goteborg (Sweden) 79	ASEA, 1912	Unknown	DE ST City
Atlantic City Tnsptn. Co. 250	Brill, 1917	Unknown	DE DT City
(Formerly Philadelphia Rapid Transit car.)			
Johnstown (PA) Traction 358	St. Louis, 1926	St. Louis EDJ-64	DE DT Lightweight city
(This car ran for many years at Stone Mountain GA. with an on-board diesel motor. It came here in 1991.)			
New York, Queensboro Bridge 601	Osgood-Bradley, 1930	Unknown	DE DT Master Unit city
(Originally believed to be a New Bedford, MA. car.)			
Brooklyn BMT 1000	Clark, 1936	Clark B-2	SE DT PCC
(On loan to Brooklyn Historic Railway Association.)			
Brussels (Belgium) MIVB/STIB 1504	Home-built, 1910	Brussels Brill 21-E	SE ST City
Boston MBTA 3204/14/16	Pullman-Standard, 1946	Clark B-2	SE DT MU PCC
Hamburg (Germany) 3584	Linke-Hoffman-Busch, 1952	Unknown	DE DT Type V6E city
Brooklyn BMT 8361	Brill, 1925	Unknown	E DT "Peter Witt" city

Staten Island Midland RR 157 (St. Louis, 1895), owned by the Old Richmondtown historic site in Staten Island, was to have gone to this museum, but in 1996 it was decided to let the Shore Line Trolley Museum of Branford CT. acquire it instead.

B. Rapid Transit Cars

Philadelphia SEPTA 127	Brill, 1927	Unknown	DE DT "Broad Street" subway
Philadelphia SEPTA 175	Pressed Steel, 1938	Unknown	DE DT "Broad Street" subway
New York Staten Island RT 353/88	Standard Steel, 1925	Unknown	DE DT Rapid transit
Philadelphia SEPTA 401/02	Brill, 1936	Unknown	DE DT "Bridge" subway
New York Staten Island RT 501	Unknown	Unknown	Unknown
New York Hudson & Manhattan 510/13	ACF, 1928	Unknown	DE DT Subway
New York IND 825	ACF, 1932	ACF 506 AB	DE DT Type R-4 subway
Brooklyn BMT "A" unit 1602A	Jewett, 1907	Unknown	DE DT "Q" subway
New York IRT 5600	ACF, 1925	Unknown	DE DT Lo-V subway
New York NYCTA 6398	ACF, 1955	Unknown	DE DT Type R-16 subway

C. Work Cars and Locomotives

Brooklyn BMT C-20	Brown Hoisting Machinery, 1905	Unknown	DE DT Electric crane
Unidentified 41	Magor, 1932	Unknown	DE DT Drill motor car
New York IRT C-211	Differential, 1932	Unknown	DE DT Crane
New York IND F-401	Magor, 1931	Unknown	DE DT Motor flat

New York-Brooklyn

1. Brooklyn Historic Railway Association, 141 Beard Street, Brooklyn NY 11231. (718) 941-3160. Standard-gauge trolley museum, not yet open to the public.

In 1980, Bob Diamond (the BHRA's president) re-discovered a long-abandoned 2000' long tunnel under Atlantic Avenue. Built in 1844 it was sealed up in 1861 and forgotten for over a century. Diamond and other volunteers formed the BHRA in 1982 and its initial months were spent surveying, excavating and cleaning the tunnel. Since the fall of 1982, BHRA members have been escorting tour groups through the tunnel's restored mid-section as a fund-raising activity. The BHRA has applied for an ISTEA grant to build a 3/4 mile trolley line from Pier 41 at the foot of Van Dyke Street Brooklyn, to the trolley museum at Beard Street Pier, and to Richards and Coffey Streets in Red Hook. Pier 41 has been restored for retail use and the Beard Street pier is now being done. The line will use Boston MBTA PCCs 3299, 3303 and 3321 (Pullman-Standard 1951). Acquired in 1993, they are being put into operating condition at the BHRA's trolley museum where 500 feet of track and wires are already up. Though not normally open to the public, visitors were treated to car rides on this short stretch on July 8, 1994. In addition to the PCCs, the BHRA has an operational 1897 Oslo car and leases Brooklyn PCC 1000 (Clark, 1936) from the Trolley Museum of New York.

2. New York Transit Subway Museum *NYCTA, 130 Livingstone Street Brooklyn, NY 11201. (718) 694-1068. Standard-gauge subway museum at Schermerhorn Street & Boerum Place in Brooklyn Heights. Open Tuesday-Sunday year-round.*

New York did not modernize its subway fleet until the 1950s and many pre-World War I veterans carried New York's masses into the 1960s. The NYCTA then recognized them as historical relics and set aside examples of most types as they came out of service. In the mid-1970s the abandoned Court Street Station, at the end of a short spur off the main IND lines, was chosen for the museum. Few transit systems can memorialize their entire history but the New York subway can, from 19th century wooden elevated cars and the first IRT steel cars of 1904, to the present day. A visitor can walk through every car and the station's lower level, a major exhibit in itself. On the upper level, exhibits and displays feature subway architectural drawings, turnstiles, tokens, maps, an operating interlocking plant in the tower (the display board shows trains running out of the nearby Hoyt/Schermerhorn Station) and a "how it works" display of a car truck, third-rail shoes, motors and brakes. A collection of Brooklyn streetcar models, built by Dr. George T. F. Rahilly, represents almost every car type except the PCC. Vintage subway operation climaxed in the 1980s with regularly-scheduled weekend "Nostalgia" Specials. Budget constraints now confine operations to occasional outings, but the museum is still fully functional. The fleet includes car 1622, A, B & C elevated cars, Q car 1910, an R-6 car, 4 BMT "A" cars, an IRT R-12 car, and B-type 2390/91/92. The NYCTA also maintains a fleet of historic buses. These are not on public display.

BUS	BUILDER AND DATE	SERIAL NUMBER
NYCTA 100	GM TDH-5301, 1959	286 (Diesel)
Fifth Avenue Coach 303	Fifth Avenue Coach Model A, 1917	– (Gasoline double-deck)
NYCTA 1059	GM TDH-5301, 1961	2560 (Diesel)
Fifth Avenue Coach 2124	Yellow Coach Model 735, 1938 100	– (Gasoline)
NYCTA 2151	GM TDH-5301, 1962	3349 (Diesel)
Fifth Avenue Coach 3100	GM TDH-5106, 1956	919 (Diesel)
NYCTA 3758	GM TDH-5303, 1963	892 (Diesel)
NYCTA 4789	GM TDH-5101, 1948	290 (Diesel)
NYCTA 5117	Flxible F2D6V-401-1, 1965	52203 (Diesel)
Manhattan-Bronx 8466	GM TDH-5303, 1967	5256 (Diesel)
NYCTA 6259	Mack C49 DT, 1956	1640 (Diesel)
NYCTA 7144	GM TDH-5106, 1957	1132 (Diesel)
NYCTA 8928	GM T6H-5305A, 1968	351 (Diesel)
NYCTA 9098	GM TDH-5106, 1958	1546 (Diesel)

Rush

New York Museum of Transportation, *PO Box 136 W. Henrietta, NY 14586. (716) 533-1113. Museum at East River Road, two miles south of exit 46 on I-90 (New York State Thruway). Standard-gauge transport museum, open Sundays year-round 11:00 a.m.-5:00 p.m.*

The museum was originally part of the "New Town" Riverton development plan of the 1960s and was to have provided both a leisure amenity to a new community and a transportation function. The new town (twelve miles south of Rochester) did not achieve its full potential, but the museum survived. Its Electrification Committee began planting poles in November, 1996.

A. City and Suburban Cars

CAR	BUILDER AND DATE	TRUCK	CAR TYPE
Batavia (NY) Traction Co. 33 Kuhlman, 1911		–	DE ST semi-convertible (body only)

(Originally Warren [PA] Street Ry. 33, to Batavia 1924, became a house in 1927, later an antique shop.)

Rochester City & Brighton RR Co. 55	Stephenson, 1867	Pedestal	SE ST Horse car

(Owned by the Rochester Museum and Science Center, who are currently storing it)

Philadelphia SEPTA (P&W) 161/168	Brill, 1927	Brill 27-MCB-2X	DE DT "Strafford" suburban

(Originally 61/68, became 161/168 in 1931. Sold to Keokuk Junction Railway in 1991.)

B. Interurban Cars

Elmira, Corning & Waverly Ry. 107	Jewett, 1911	Standard C-55	DE DT Interurban coach
NY State Rys. Utica Lines 60	Cincinnati, 1916	Baldwin	DE DT Interurban coach

(This car served the Rochester subway and is owned by and stored at the NY State museum in Albany.)

NY State Rys. Rochester & Estn. 157	Niles, 1914	Brill 27-MCB-3X	SE DT Interurban coach
Northern Texas Traction 409	St. Louis, 1919	–	DE DT Interurban coach (body only)

(Originally a trailer, later motorized, became parlor car in 1925. Body cosmetically restored and used in the Rochester Spaghetti Warehouse restaurant. Transferred to museum September 1996, after the restaurant closed.)

C. Work Cars and Locomotives

N.Y. State Rys	Rochester 0243	Stephenson, 1891	Peckham 11 (probably) DE ST Sand car

(Formerly Rochester car 162, originally ton McGuire "Columbian" truck. Acquired used Peckham truck in 1927. Presently under restoration and serves as an exhibit in a diorama on car construction.)

Philadelphia SEPTA C-130	Brill, 1923	Brill 50-E-2	DE DT Snow sweeper

(Originally Phildalphia RT wing plow E-217, became snow sweeper 1925.)

D. Motor Buses

BUS	BUILDER AND DATE	SERIAL NUMBER MOTOR
Rochester (NY) Transit 233	GM TDH-5304, 1963	104 (Diesel)
Syracuse (NY) Transit 734	Twin Coach 34S, 1946	293B (Gasoline)

NORTH CAROLINA

Charlotte

Charlotte Trolley Inc., *2104 South Boulevard, Charlotte, NC 28203. (704) 375-0850. Standard-gauge tourist trolley runs Friday-Sunday all year 10:00 a.m.- 9:00 p.m. (6:00 p.m. Sunday) and available for groups and charters at all times.*

A project to restore Charlotte 85 (Charlotte's last streetcar in 1938) was completed May 7, 1994 when it ran on 50 yards of track outside the barn at Atherton Mill shopping center. On September 16, 1994, another 150 yards came into service and now nearly 300 yards are wired north of the barn. A further 1 1/2 miles will be done once purchase of a disused Norfolk Southern RR track is agreed. Presently this section is leased from the railroad. From August 1996 to March 1997, it was used for revenue operation, cars towing a generator trailer. An extension to the Convention Center awaits a railroad bridge replacement at Stonewall Street.

CAR	BUILDER AND DATE	TRUCK	CAR TYPE
Charlotte 1	UEC, 1911	UEC compensating	DE ST City

(Originally Piraeus [Greece], Hellenic Electric Railway 60.)

Charlotte, Southern Public Utilities 85	Home-built, 1927	Unknown	DE DT City

Spencer

Spencer Shops (North Carolina Transportation Museum), *PO Box 165 Spencer, NC 28159. (704) 636-2889. Standard-gauge railroad museum owned and operated by Historic Sites Section of NC Dept. of Cultural Resources. Museum at 411 S. Salisbury Avenue, Spencer, three miles north of Salisbury off I-85. Open daily April-October, Tuesday-Sunday November-March.*

Spencer Shops was the Southern Railroad's largest repair facility. The restored shops serve as a railroad museum, with a large variety of interpretive displays. The collection also includes two streetcars, unidentified at press-time.

Bellevue

Mad River and NKP RR Museum, *233 York Street, Bellevue, OH 44811-1377. (419) 483-2222. Open Wednesday-Sunday June-August, weekends in May, September and October, 1:00 p.m.- 5:00 p.m.*

Established in 1976 as a museum of small-town railroading, many exhibits are located inside rolling stock and railroad-related buildings on the site. The museum owns Cleveland RTA PCC 4665 (originally Cleveland TS 4240, later Toronto TTC Type A-11 4650) and two unidentified interurban bodies from Ohio's Lake Shore Electric Railway, one of which is now being restored.

Chippewa Lake

Northern Ohio Trolley Museum, *PO Box 458, Chippewa Lake, OH 44215-0458. Standard-gauge trolley museum at Buffham Road, Chippewa Lake. Not yet open to the public.*

NORM began in 1965 when three men bought a caboose. The first trolleys were bought soon after and stored at the Brookins museum in Olmsted Falls. The Buffham Road site was bought to supplement a two-mile stretch of former Cleveland Southwestern interurban right-of-way purchased in 1977. The museum exists "to collect, preserve, restore, display and operate streetcars and other railway equipment for use by the public." Though a significant regional collection has been amassed, all exhibits are in open-air storage, on two closely-located sites. There are presently no overhead wires and little track, but the first buildings were being erected in early 1997.

A. City and Suburban Cars

CAR	BUILDER AND DATE	TRUCK	CAR TYPE
Shaker Heights RT (OH) 3/11/031	Kuhlman, 1914	Brill 51-E-1	SE DT Center-entrance city
(Originally Cleveland Railway 1203/11/31. 1211 ended Shaker service as a wrecker. 1231 became Shaker greaser car 031.)			
Cleveland RTA (Shaker Rapid) 49	St. Louis, 1946	Clark B-2	SE DT MU PCC
(Originally St. Louis PS 1775.)			
Cleveland RTA (Shaker Rapid) 72/78/81/83/86/92	Pullman-Standard, 1947	Clark B-2	SE DT MU PCC
Pittsburgh PAT 1644 (later 1797 II)	St. Louis, 1945	St. Louis B-3	SE DT PCC
Toronto TTC 2778	CCF, 1923	CCF 3550	SE DT Type P-1 small "Peter Witt" city
Cleveland RTA (Shaker) 4655/56	Pullman-Standard, 1946	Clark B-2	SE DT MU PCC
(Originally Cleveland TS 4230/21, later Toronto TTC Type A-11 4655/56.)			

B. Interurban and Electric Freight Cars

Cincinnati & Lake Erie 101/05	Kuhlman, 1927	–	DE DT Combine (body only)
Lake Shore Electric (OH) 181	Jewett, 1918	–	DE DT Interurban coach (body only)
Cleveland Southwestern 51	Unknown builder and date	–	DE DT Freight motor (body only)
Northern Ohio Traction & Light 1510/15/19	Kuhlman, 1920	–	DE DT Interurban coach (body only)
Lake Shore Electric 464	Home-built, 1919	–	DE DT Automobile trailer (body only)

C. Rapid Transit Cars

Philadelphia SEPTA 12	Brill, 1927	Unknown	DE DT Broad Street subway
Cleveland TS 112	St. Louis, 1955	General Steel	DE DT PCC rapid transit
Cleveland TS 201/02	St. Louis, 1955	General Steel	SE DT PCC rapid transit
Cleveland TS 265/66	St. Louis, 1958	General Steel	SE DT PCC Rapid transit
Chicago CTA 4043/4423	Cincinnati, 1914/1924	Baldwin 78-30	DE DT Rapid transit

D. Work Cars and Locomotives

PIttsburgh PAT M-30	McGuire, 1896	Unknown	DE ST Snow Sweeper
Cleveland RTA 0518	Differential, 1927	Unknown	DE DT Dump car

| Cleveland RTA 0610/11/15 | Differential, 1928 | Unknown | DE DT Flat cars |
| Cleveland RTA (Shaker) 0710/11 | Differential, 1925 | Unknown | DE DT Crane |

E. Electric Trolley Buses
Dayton CTC 604 (originally Kansas City PS 2553) Marmon-Herrington TC 44, 1947

F. Motor Buses

BUS	BUILDER AND DATE	SERIAL NUMBER
Berea (OH) Bus Lines 190	GM SDH-5302, 1966	051 (Diesel)
Detroit DSR 1321	GM TDH-5105, 1955	1449 (Diesel)

Cincinnati

1. Cincinnati Street Railway, 7125 Reading Road, Cincinnati, OH 45237-3806. (513) 631-2690. Proposed tourist trolley.

Established in 1990, the CSR proposes vintage trolleys for the Riverfront, downtown and Over-the-Rhine districts, key areas of Cincinnati's urban and economic core. As part of the overall metropolitan transportation web, the line would be a local circulator and possibly a part of the light rail system now being planned. The CSR owns four Pittsburgh PCC cars, bought in 1993.

2. Cincinnati Transit Historical Association, Box 141381, Cincinnati, OH 45250. (513) 681-4219.

Though still served by Amtrak passenger trains, the stunning Art Deco Cincinnati Union Station building is now a cultural center housing local and natural history museums. The CTHA owns Cincinnati 2435 (body only, Cincinnati, 1923), displayed in the south wing of the station as part of a local history exhibit on World War II in the city. In 1991, the CTHA bought Pittsburgh PCC 1761, restoring it as Cincinnati SR 1175 (the next number after Cincinnati's own highest-numbered PCC). The CTHA also owns Ohio Bus lines 211 (GM SDH-4501, 1960, serial number 012), an unidentified Columbus GM bus and an unidentified Flxible bus.

Cleveland

1. Greater Cleveland Regional Transit Authority, 615 Superior Avenue NW, Cleveland, OH 44113. (216) 566-5100. Standard-gauge rapid transit and light rail.

The former Shaker Heights Rapid, now the RTA's Blue and Green light rail lines, maintains two heritage cars for occasional charter or special event service, plus a work car. The recent extension of the Blue and Green Lines from Tower City along the Waterfront line (formally opened July 10, 1996) serving the Flats and the Municipal Stadium has been a phenomenal success. A tourist trolley was one of the alternatives originally proposed for this extension, the first on the former Shaker Heights Rapid in many decades.

CAR	BUILDER AND DATE	TRUCK	CAR TYPE
Cleveland RTA (Shaker Rapid) 12, 024	Kuhlman, 1914	Brill 51-E-1	SE DT center-entrance city
(Originally Cleveland Ry. 1212/17, leased to Shaker 1920/21, bought by Shaker 1940, renumbered 12/17. 17 later line car 024.)			
Cleveland RTA (Shaker Rapid) 76	Pullman-Standard, 1947	Clark B-2	SE DT MU PCC

Cleveland RTA (Shaker Rapid) greaser car 031 (Kuhlman, 1914), went to the Northern Ohio Trolley Museum at Chippewa Lake in 1996.

2. Trolleyville USA (Gerald E. Brookins Museum of Electric Railways), 7100 Columbia Road, Olmsted Twp., OH 44138. (216) 235-4725. Standard-gauge trolley museum. Cars run Sundays and holidays Memorial Day-end of September 1:00 p.m.- 5:00 p.m., plus Wednesday and Friday June-August 10:00 a.m.- 3:00 p.m. Group charters can be arranged any weekday between April and October.

Trolleyville began as a tourist line providing internal transport to an upscale mobile-home park.

Car acquisition began in 1954 and the first runs were made in 1962 under the name Columbia Park and Southwestern. Gerald E. Brookins, the owner, quickly found that while the cars were popular, it was the public, not park residents, who were riding and Trolleyville became a museum, collecting and running vintage cars and amassing archival and research library materials on mass transit. Trolleyville's strengths are its Ohio city cars and an unrivalled Chicago, Aurora and Elgin interurban car collection. It is also one of the most attractively landscaped and manicured of all the "green fields" trolley museums.

A. City and Suburban Cars

CAR	BUILDER AND DATE	TRUCK	CAR TYPE
Vera Cruz (Mexico) 9/19	Brill, 1908	Brill 21-E	SE DT 10-bench open
(Possibly 1895 cars for a Philadelphia street railway company.)			
Cleveland RTA (Shaker Rapid) 63	St. Louis, 1947	Clark B-2	SE DT MU PCC
(Originally TCRT 352.)			
Cleveland RTA (Shaker Rapid) 71/86	Pullman-Standard, 194	Clark B-2	SE DT MU PCC
Blackpool (England) Corp. 147	Hurst Nelson, 1924	Blackpool/Hurst Nelson "Preston"	DE DT Double- -deck city
Shaker Heights Rapid 1218/25	Kuhlman, 1913	Brill 51-E-1	SE DT Center-entrance city
(Originally Cleveland Railways 1218/25.)			
Cincinnati Street Ry. 2227	Cincinnati, 1915	Cincinnati/Elliott 50-D	SE DT City
Cleveland Ry. 2365	Home-built, 1917	Unknown	DE DT Trailer
Boston MBTA 3334	Pullman-Standard, 1945	Clark B-2	DE DT PCC
(Originally Dallas Railway & Terminal 612.)			
Pittsburgh Rlwys 4145	Pressed Steel, 1911	Standard C-80P	SE DT Jones high-floor city
Toronto TTC 4602	St. Louis/CCF, 1951	Clark B-2	SE DT Type A-15 PCC
(Originally Toronto TTC Type A-8 4537.)			

Cleveland RTA (Shaker) PCC 74 (in poor condition) has been deaccessioned and stripped for parts. Its standard-gauge trucks went to Toronto TTC PCC 4602. Cleveland RTA (Shaker) PCC 75 and the body of Toledo Community Traction & Light 585 (American, 1911) were deaccessioned and auctioned during 1996. Seven unaccessioned Cleveland RTA ex-Shaker Heights PCCs on the property belong to the brokerage company Vintage Electric Streetcar of Windber PA. and were intended for a proposed tourist trolley line in Frederick MD.

B. Interurban and Electric Freight Cars

Aurora, Elgin & Chicago 36 (Shaker Rapid) 76	Stephenson, 1902	Baldwin 84-25MCB	DE DT Interurban coach
Fostoria and Fremont (OH) 40	Colman, 1923	–	DE DT Combine (body only)
Centerville, Sthn. Iowa Utilities 100/01	American, 1914/1915	Brill 27-MCB	DE DT Box motor
(Originally Centerville, Albia & Southern cars.)			
Aurora, Elgin & Fox River 302-4, 306	St. Louis, 1924	St. Louis EIB 64	DE DT Lightweight interurban coach
(Later Shaker Heights 302-04/06.)			
Aurora, Elgin & Chicago 303 (later CA&E 303)	Niles, 1906	Pullman MCB	DE DT Interurban coach
Chicago, Aurora & Elgin 319	Kuhlman, 1909	Baldwin 84-35 MCB	DE DT Interurban coach
Chicago, Aurora & Elgin 409	Pullman, 1923	Pullman MCB	DE DT Interurban coach
Chicago, Aurora & Elgin 451/53/58/6	St. Louis, 1945	General Steel MCB	DE DT Interurban coach
(Car 451 is painted and lettered as Columbia Park and Southwestern 451.)			
Toledo Ry. & Lt. "Toledo"	Home-built, 1906	–	SE DT Interurban parlor car (body only)

The body of Lorain & Cleveland Electric Railway interurban 83 (Brill, 1898) was deaccessioned and auctioned during 1996.

C. Work Cars and Locomotives

Centerville, Sthn. Iowa Utilities 1	Home-built, 1896	Peckham	DE ST Line car
Cleveland RTS OX	Kuhlman, 1924	Unknown	DE DT Express motor/utility
(Originally Michigan Electric Ry. 200 or 201, then Northern Ohio Traction & Light 1078, Shaker 78 in 1932.)			

Columbus

Ohio Historical Society/Ohio Village *(next door to Ohio Historical Center), 1982 Velma Avenue, Columbus, OH. 43211-2497 (I-71 and E. 17th Avenue). (614) 297-2613.*

The Ohio Historical Center contains the Ohio Historical Preservation Office, a library, state archives and exhibits on Ohio history, environment and archaelogy. The adjacent Ohio Village recreates an 1860s Ohio town, where costumed interpreters reenact daily life of the period. The village owns two Columbus single-truck Stephenson-built horse cars of the early 1880s which were electrified in the early 1890s; open car 3 with a Brill truck, closed city car 6 with a Dupont. They were sold in 1896 to the Lancaster (PA) Traction Co., where they ran as cars 3 and 6 until the Lancaster system closed in 1937. They have been stored complete and under cover since then. Plans exist to conserve car 3 in its present condition as a static display. Car 6, in poorer condition, will be rebuilt and perhaps converted back to horse traction for use on a line in Ohio Village.

Dayton

Carillon Historical Park (Educational & Musical Arts Inc), *2001 South Patterson Blvd. Dayton, OH 45409 (513) 293-2841. Static displays, open year-round 9:00 a.m. to 5:00 p.m.*

Donated in the early 1940s by Edward A. Deeds (Chairman of the National Cash Register Company), and his wife Edith Deeds as a gift to the city of Dayton, the park's centerpiece is a Belgian Carillon, which was dedicated on Easter Sunday, 1942. Deeds then began collecting historical material and artifacts on Dayton history, anxious that children should feel the excitement of the city's past through a hands-on knowledge of suitably displayed relics. Transport exhibits include Dayton-built autos, steam locomotives, passenger cars and cabooses, buildings and businesses of early times plus a replica of the Wright Brothers' bicycle shop.

CAR	BUILDER AND DATE	TRUCK	CAR TYPE
Toledo, Pt. Clinton & Lakeside Ry. 2	Kuhlman, 1904	Unknown	DE DT Interurban coach
Dayton City Rlwy. 123 (Originally Sao Paulo (Brazil) 471.)	Brill, 1913	Brill 21-E	DE ST 11-bench open
Dayton City Transit 515	Marmon-Herrington TC 48, 1949		ETB

Orrville

Ohio Museum of Transportation, *PO Box 771230 Lakewood, OH 44107-0051. Bus museum with operational exhibits, open Sundays Memorial Day to Labor Day, noon-6:00 p.m.*

Established in 1990, this developing museum focuses on Greater Cleveland and Ohio. Many of its buses are run on fan trips and around the museum site just off South Crown Hill at Orrville, OH. This site is rented and a permanent home is being sought.

A. Electric Trolley Bus

BUS	BUILDER AND DATE	SERIAL NUMBER
Dayton City Transit Co 604 (Originally Kansas City PS 2553.)	Marmon-Herrington TC 44, 1947	10268

B. Motor Buses

City of Euclid 38	GM TDH-4509, 1952	2093 (Diesel)
Berea Bus line 54	White 798, 1946	31688 (body only)
Berea Bus Line 78	White 1144-1, 1951	374356 (Gasoline)
Pittsburgh & Weirton (WV) 98 (Originally Steubenville OH 525.)	GM TDH-3612, 1951	817 (Diesel)
Fidelity Motor Bus (Massilon OH) 100	GM TGH-3102, 1953	082 (Gasoline)
Indian Trails (Owosso MI) 121	GM PD-4104, 1960	4998 (Diesel)
North Olmsted 150	GM T8H-5305, 1971	453 (Diesel)
Toledo RTA 201	AM General 9635B, 1978	475 (Diesel)
North Olmsted 213	GM T8H-5307A, 1976	3726 (Diesel)
Hamilton (OH) The Bus Co., 302	GM TDH-3502, 1968	102 (Diesel)
Columbus Transit 350	Twin Coach FL 30, 1952	33 (Gasoline)
Lakewood (OH) Rapid Transit 404 (Originally Cleveland Transit 3787.)	Twin Coach 41-S, 1947	261 (Gasoline)

Toledo RTA 407	Flxible 111DD-D51, 1971	55629 (Diesel)
Cleveland CTS 430	GM TDH-5103, 1953	915 (Diesel)
Maple Heights (OH) 470	GM TDH-5303	5842 (Diesel)
Akron Metro 588, 589	Flxible 45102, 1978	64097 (Diesel)
(589 was the last Flxible "New-look" bus made.)		
Toledo RTA 611	GM T6H-4523A, 1976	1693 (Diesel)
Cleveland CTS 641	GM TDH-5301, 1959	119 (Diesel)
(Became Fullington Auto Bus [OH] 378 in 1968.)		
Dayton RTA 817	GM T6H-4521A, 1971	811 (Diesel)
(Originally Avenue B and Broadway {NY} 623.)		
Cleveland RTA 873	GM TDH-5303, 1963	1354 (Diesel)
(Originally Atlanta 873.)		
Lehigh Valley 1250	ACF H-15-S, 1936	S115 (Gasoline)
(Originally Harrisburg {PA} Rys. 425.)		
Maple Heights (OH) 1305	GM TDH-5105, 1955	1449 (Diesel)
(Originally Detroit Street Railways 1321.)		
Cleveland RTA 2105	GM TDH-5303, 1967	5891 (Diesel)
(Later became Greater Cleveland RTA Zoo bus.)		
Cleveland RTA 2609	GM T8H-5307A, 1975	2612 (Diesel)
Cleveland CTS 2801	Mack C50DT, 1951	402 (Diesel)
(Originally numbered 2701 with gasoline motor.)		
Cleveland CTS 2987	White 1150DW, 1953	396052 (Diesel)
Cleveland Transit 3028	Flxible 111DD-D5, 1969	53891 (Diesel)
D. C. Transit 3167	GM TGH-3102, 1958	872 (Gasoline)
Cleveland CTS 3666	Twin Coach 44-S, 1947	007 (Gasoline)
D.C. Transit 4240	White 788, 1940	225530 (Gasoline)
Cleveland RTA 8008	AM General 10240B, 1978	011307 (Diesel)
Hagey Bus Lines (PA).	Flxible Clipper, 1946	7629 (body only)
Newcastle (PA) Smeal Bus lines (unnumbered)	Reo 96-HT, 1945	7029 (body only)

Pataskala

Buckeye Lake Trolley, *475 South Main Street, Pataskala, OH 43062. (614) 927-4985. Private collection of over 40 streetcars and interurbans, not open to the public. This roster is incomplete.*

A. City and Suburban Cars

CAR	BUILDER AND DATE	TRUCK	CAR TYPE
Cleveland RTA (Shaker Rapid) 40/41	St. Louis, 1946	Clark B-2	SE DT MU PCC
(Originally St. Louis PS 1771, 1769.)			
Cleveland RTA (Shaker Rapid) 77/79/80/84/91/95	Pullman-Standard, 1947	Clark B-2	SE DT MU PCC
Pittsburgh PAT 1976	St. Louis, 1945	Clark B-2	SE DT PCC
(Originally 1603, then 1784 II. Rebuilt with flat front in 1975.)			
Cleveland RTA (Shaker) 4662/63	Pullman-Standard, 1946	Clark B-2	SE DT MU PCC
(Formerly Cleveland TS 4237/38, then Toronto TTC Type A-11 4662/63.)			

B. Interurban Cars

Columbus Delaware & Marion (OH) 500	ACF, 1926	Baldwin 84-34AA	SE DT Interurban Parlor

C. Buses

BUS	BUILDER AND DATE	SERIAL NUMBER
Columbus (OH) Transit 626	Marmon-Herrington TC48, 1948	10470 (ETB)
Lewisburg, Milton & Watsontown (PA) Pass. Ry. 20	Mack AC, 1921	6000S (Gasoline)

Worthington

Ohio Railway Museum, *PO Box 171, Worthington, OH 43085. (614) 885-7345. Standard-gauge railroad and trolley museum on Proprietor's Road, just off route 161 in Worthington, OH. Open Sundays Memorial day-end of October.*

The Central Ohio Railfans Association was formed in 1945 and in 1946 received an interurban coach, donated by a local NRHS chapter. A member owned land at the present site and CORA moved in during 1948 to establish an operating rail transit museum. The first car ran in the early 1950s and until 1978, railroad equipment was also operated. Suburban encroachment on this former green fields site compelled abandonment of 1/4 mile of track north of the museum in the 1980s. The ORM operated infrequently in the early 1990s and ceased in 1994 so it could equip itself to meet new FRA standards. Instead, activity was turned to organizing steam railroad trips, which were popular and remunerative until CSX recently eliminated steam. Attention has now returned to the streetcars. The highway 161 bridge, built by the museum in 1954, has been redecked, a new solid-state substation installed and regular operation (with PCC 1772) resumed in 1995.

A. City and Suburban Cars

CAR	BUILDER AND DATE	TRUCK	CAR TYPE
Illinois Terminal 450	St. Louis, 1949	St. Louis B-3	DE DT MU Suburban PCC
Kansas City, Metropolitan St. Ry. 472	Brownell, 1900	Dupont 46	DE ST City
(Later Kansas City PS railgrinder 068.)			
Columbus (OH) Rlwy. P&L 703	Kuhlman, 1925	CCF 3550	DE DT City
Pittsburgh PAT 1772	St. Louis, 1949	Clark B-2	SE DT PCC
Detroit Street Railway 3876	St. Louis, 1931	St. Louis M-66	SE DT "Peter Witt" city

Toronto TTC Type A-9 PCC 4558 (originally Cincinnati CST 1158 St. Louis, 1947) and Toronto TTC Type A-11 MU PCC 4630 (originally Cleveland CTS 4205, sold back to Cleveland as 4630 by Toronto for use on RTS Shaker Rapid in 1977) were acquired in 1982 and scrapped by the museum in 1993/94.

B. Interurban Cars

Ohio PS 21	Niles, 1905	Peckham 40A MCB	SE DT Combine
(Originally Toledo, Port Clinton & Lakeside Rlwy. 21, later Northwestern Ohio Rlwy. 21.)			
Ohio PS 41	Kuhlman, 1925	Brill 77-EX	SE DT Lightweight interurban
(Later numbered 64, then became Ohio Edison Company car.)			
Cincinnati & Lake Erie 119	Cincinnati, 1930	Cincinnati ABC74D	SE DT Lightweight interurban
Later Cedar Rapids & Iowa City Railway 119.)			
Chicago North Shore & Milwaukee 154	Brill, 1915	Baldwin 84-30A	DE DT Interurban coach
Columbus, Delaware & Marion 501	ACF, 1926	Baldwin 84-34AA	SE DT Interurban parlor

C. Rapid Transit Cars

Chicago CTA 4441/49	Cincinnati, 1924	Baldwin 78-30	DE DT Elevated

D. Work Cars and Locomotives

Columbus (OH) Ry. P&L 2	Home-built, 1926	Brill 27-MCB-2X	DE DT Steeple cab locomotive
(Later Columbus & Sthn. Ohio Electric 2, used to haul coal to the Pickaway power plant.)			
Youngstown & Ohio River 7	Baldwin/WH, 1922	Baldwin MCB	DE DT Steeple cab locomotive
(Originally Omaha, Lincoln & Beatrice Rlwy. 2 in 1933, Cornwall [ON] St. Rlwy 11 in 1947.)			
Eastern Michigan 7763	Detroit United, 1923	Peckham 14-AXX	DE DT Line car
(Originally a Detroit United Railway car, became Eastern Michigan car in 1928 and Shaker Heights [OH] RT 101 in 1932.)			

Toronto TTC Crane C-2 (home-built, 1921, Baldwin 78-30 trucks) was acquired for parts. Columbus (OH) Ry. P&L DE DT Center-cab flat car 067 (Home-built, 1924, Peckham trucks) and Philadelphia SEPTA DE DT Snow Sweeper C-124 (Brill, 1924, Brill 50E-1 trucks) are no longer part of the collection. There present whereabouts is unknown.

OKLAHOMA

McAlester

Oklahoma Trolley Association c/o M. Pruitt, 213 East Madison, McAlester, OK 74501. (918) 423-6408. Private collection, not open to the public.

The OTA owns the bodies of Southwest Missouri ERR interurban 49 (Home-built 1908), a Pittsburg County Traction Company Niles-built car body, the shell of a Tulsa (OK) Birney "safety" car and the body of Texas Electric Box motor 53.

OREGON

Portland

1. **Tri-Met** *4012 SE 17th Avenue, Portland, OR 97202. (503) 238-4834. Standard-gauge replica tourist trolley runs on light rail route between downtown and Lloyd Center, weekends March-May, daily June-December. No service January and February.*

In the mid-1980s, when Portland's tourist trolley service was being planned, it was clear the original wood-bodied Portland "Council Crest" Brill semi-convertibles proposed risked serious damage if hit by a light rail car. Portland businessmen Bill and Sam Naito acquired Oporto cars 114/67/78/81/89 from Portugal, should they get the franchise. They didn't, due to ridership on Tri-Met's line exceeding projections and worry that Oporto cars would be unequal to the demands placed on them. Tri-Met ordered three new collision-resistant replicas of the "Council Crest" cars (a fourth car was ordered later) which began running on November 29, 1991 and the Naitos then sold their Oporto cars. Car 178 (painted yellow and numbered 819) was displayed on light rail tracks between June 1985 and April 1986, stored at Tri-Met's Ruby Junction carhouse until July 1989, then went to northwest Portland for display at the Montgomery Park retail center. In 1989, car 167 was traded to BC Transit for Hong Kong 3' 6" gauge single-truck double-deck car 12 (home-built, 1952). Cars 114/78/81 were sold to Memphis in November 1993 for restoration. Car 189 went to San Francisco where it is part of MUNI's historic trolley fleet. The Hong Kong car is believed to remain in Portland.

CAR	BUILDER AND DATE	TRUCK	CAR TYPE
Portland 511-514	Gomaco, 1991	Clark B-2	DE DT Replica Brill semi-convertible

(Replica bodies with trucks, motors and controls from Chicago 6000-class PCC rapid transit cars.)

2. **Vintage Trolley Inc.,** *115 NW First Avenue, Portland, OR 97209. (503) 323-7363.*

Vintage Trolley Inc (VTI) runs tourist trolleys on Tri-Met's light rail line, acts as a fund-raiser, collects donations and arranges corporate sponsorships. Fund-raising has been of greater importance since fares were abolished on the tourist cars and ridership went up substantially.

3. **Willamette Shore Trolley,** *operated by Oregon Electric Railway Historical Society, PO Box 308 Lake Oswego, OR 97034. Standard gauge tourist trolley on 6.75 miles of former Southern Pacific interurban between Portland and Lake Oswego. Cars powered by a portable generator. Several trips daily June-Labor Day, weekends March-May, September-December.*

Six miles of former Southern Pacific RR interurban trackage between Portland and Lake Oswego, used for freight until closed in 1984, was earmarked as a light rail southern extension. To protect the integrity of the right-of-way, some form of rail operation had to continue until completion of the purchase otherwise it would be regarded as abandoned, giving local owners the chance to reclaim portions of line adjacent to their property. If that happened, the line could never be reused for rail purposes. With Tri-Met already planning tourist cars on its new light rail line, why not do the same here? There were no overhead wires but a diesel generator towed by a car would take care of traction problems. A January 1987 press conference and a short test run with OERHS Portland "Council Crest" car 503 proved the idea sound and OERHS signed a four-month operating contract for 1987. But Portland 503 had wood rot in its end sills, a serious structural defect needing major repair. Instead, Blackpool double-deck car 48 made the first runs on September 12, 1987. Operations ceased in December but with their case proved, Portland (and other interested authorities) paid $1,200,00 to the SP to "land-bank" the tracks. Several charter trips were run and in 1990 Gales Creek Enterprises (now known as Streetcar Investment Group) contracted to run the line. Their fleet included San Antonio 300 (American, 1913) and Blackpool (England) 731 (home-built, 1959) an illuminated car named "Blackpool Belle," built on former Blackpool open 163 of 1927. When GCE's contract ended in 1994, a new OERHS operating contract was signed.

Blackpool 48 was transferred by rail (under its own power) back to the line in summer 1995 and was later joined by Portland 813. Recently the line was extended south into downtown Lake Oswego and a short northern extension (from Portland's Moody Avenue to Riverplace) was dedicated on April 25, 1997.

4. Oregon Trolley Institute/Streetcar Investment Group *61635 NW Agaard Road, Gales Creek, OR 97117. (503) 357-3954. Private collection, not open to the public.*

The Oregon Trolley Institute and the Streetcar Investment Group succeeded the former Gales Creek Enterprises streetcar brokerage and restoration business of Paul Class, originally of Glenwood OR., more recently of Tillamook OR. The OTI owns several cars which are available to customers for restoration, including Melbourne (Australia) Type W5 cars 756 and 799 (home-built 1936, 1937, M&MTB Type 15 trucks). A recent acquisition has been Toronto TTC Type A-7 MU PCC car 4478 (St. Louis/CCF, 1949). Other cars include Ballarat (Australia) 30, three Oporto (Portugal) cars and a Seattle-Tacoma interurban body. Some or all may be moved for further storage at the Glenwood site now being vacated by the Oregon Electric Railway Historical Society.

PENNSYLVANIA

Hummelstown

Middletown & Hummelstown RR., 136 Brown Street, Middletown, PA 17057. (717) 944-4435. Tourist railroad, open weekends June-October, Tuesday-Friday July and August.

This short-line railroad (also known as the "milk and honey line") switches freight in the Middletown area and runs tourist passenger trains on a former Reading RR branch. Railroad cars and trolleys are stored around the station. One disconnected track is 5' 2 1/2" gauge for the Philadelphia cars. A heritage trolley proposal is on hold. This roster is incomplete.

A. City and Suburban Cars

CAR	BUILDER AND DATE	TRUCK	CAR TYPE
Hershey (PA) Transit 4 *(Originally an Ephrata and Lebanon [PA] car.)*	Cincinnati, unknown date	Unknown	DE DT City
Philadelphia SEPTA (Red Arrow) 77/83/4/6	Brill, 1932	Brill 89-E-1	DE DT Lightweight suburban
York (PA) Railways 162 *(A rare Brill copy of a Cincinnati Car Co. curved-side design.)*	Brill, 1924	–	DE DT curved side city
Dallas Ry. & Tmnl. 605 *(Became Boston MBTA 3323 in 1959.)*	Pullman-Standard, 1945	Clark B-2	DE DT PCC
Rio de Janeiro (Brazil) 441	Unknown	Unknown	DE ST 10-bench open
Rio de Janeiro (Brail) 1719	Home-built, 1912	Unknown	DE DT 13-bench open
Philadelphia SEPTA 2095/2104/2725	St. Louis, 1948 (2725, 1947)	Clark B-2	SE DT PCC

B. Rapid Transit Cars

Philadelphia SEPTA (P&W) 476/77 *(Originally Chicago Transit Authority rapid transit cars.)*	St. Louis, 1951	Unknown	DE DT PCC rapid transit

C. Work cars and locomotives

Kansas City PS 2 (or 66)	Unknown	Unknown	DE DT Locomotive
Philadelphia SEPTA C-121	Brill, 1923	Brill 50-E-2	DE DT Snowsweeper
Brooklyn BMT 9425	Unknown	Unknown	DE DT Freight motor

An unidentified single-truck car and two Chicago (EL) work cars are also owned.

Johnstown

Vintage Electric Streetcar Company (Vesco), *1400 Somerset Avenue, Windber, PA 15963. (814) 467-4108. Private collection, not open to the public.*

VESCO is a brokerage operation that has acquired cars for resale and for use on tourist trolley projects. Most cars are stored on a Johnstown and Stoney Creek RR siding at Moxham. The Toronto

PCCs were bought in 1996, but may be resold (except 4524 and 4529) to Kenosha WI. for a planned tourist trolley line.

A. City and Suburban Cars

CARS	BUILDER AND DATE	TRUCK	CAR TYPE
Philadelphia SEPTA (Red Arrow) 20/22	St. Louis, 1949	St. Louis	DE DT MU Suburban PCC
Cleveland RTA (Shaker Heights) 56/58	St. Louis, 1947	Clark B-2	SE DT MU PCC
(Originally Twin Cities Rapid Transit 345/47.)			
Cleveland RTA (Shaker Heights) 73/77/87/91/93	Pullman-Standard, 1947	Clark B-2	SE DT MU PCC
Pittsburgh PAT 1703/38/41/50/54/71	St. Louis, 1949	Clark B-2B (St. Louis B-3 on 1703)	SE DT PCC
Philadelphia SEPTA 2103	St. Louis, 1948	Clark B-2	SE DT PCC
Philadelphia SEPTA 2258/59/61/69-71/74/79/83/90	St. Louis, 194	Clark B-2	SE DT PCC
(Originally Kansas City PS 761,797,786,733,736,777,763,731,734,752 respectively.)			
Boston MBTA 3229/42/44/46 47+/52+/55+ 3256+/59/61+/66/67/70+/71+ (+ = 1946)	Pullman-Standard, 1945	Clark B-2	SE DT MU PCC
Philadelphia SEPTA 2724	St. Louis, 1947	Clark B-2	SE DT PCC
Toronto TTC 4524/29	St. Louis/CCF, 1951	Clark B-2	SE DT Type A-8 PCC
Toronto TTC 4606/09 4610/15/16	St. Louis/CCF, 1951	Clark B-2	SE DT Type A-15 PCC
(Originally Toronto TTC Type A-8 4528, 4526, 4541, 4518, 4515 respectively.)			

B. Rapid Transit Cars

Philadelphia SEPTA (P&W) 478-481, 484-489	St. Louis, 1951	Clark B-2	SE DT PCC Rapid transit
(Originally Chicago Transit Authority 6000-6199 class cars.)			

C. Work Cars

Boston MBTA 3285	Pullman-Standard, 1951	Clark B-2	DE DT PCC Line car
Boston MBTA 3326	Pullman-Standard, 1945	Clark B-2	DE DT PCC Sand car
(Originally Dallas Railway & Terminal 621.)			

Leesport

Reading Company Technical and Historical Society PO Box 15143, Reading, PA 19107-5143. (610) 926-0253. Owns the Reading Railway Museum. Most vehicles kept at Wall and Canal Street in Leesport PA, six miles north of Reading and just off state route 161. Museum open weekends Memorial Day to Labor Day noon- 5:00 p.m.

In addition to more than 40 pieces of historic railroad equipment, the Historical Society owns the body of Reading Transit double-end double-truck lightweight city car 807 (home-built, 1924), a copy of Boston's type 5 lightweight city car. In 1994, the RCTHS bought a Boston Type 5 car (believed to be 5777, Osgood-Bradley, 1923) from the Connecticut Trolley Museum at Warehouse Point for spares to restore the Reading car. Additionally, the RCTHS owns Reading Street Railway (and successor company) buses 651 (GM, 1949), 678 (GM, 1960) and 923 (GM, 1975).

Ligonier

Idlewild Park/Kennywood Park, Ligonier, PA. 15658. Replica tourist horse cars, 3' gauge.

The park runs two replica 8-bench open horse cars built by Gales Creek Enterprises of Oregon in 1987 for the Indianapolis Zoo. In Indianapolis the cars were too heavy for one-horse operation and two horses blocked the pathways along which they traveled. They were sold by the Zoo in Fall, 1988. In Pennsylvania, they were converted to low voltage third rail electric cars, using a 15 HP three-phase motor and a reduction gearbox with chain and sprocket drive powering one axle.

Mannheim

Mannheim Historical Society. c/o Professor W. B. Rhoades Art History Dept. SUNY 75 South Mannheim Blvd. New Paltz, NY 12561. No further information.

This ad-hoc group has several hundred feet of track to run restored Conestoga (Lancaster PA) Traction Birney 236 (Brill, 1926). The group also owns Philadelphia PTC "Peter Witt" 8530, bought when taken out of service in 1957. At one time, the Birney was moved from the Landis Farm Museum to be displayed at the former Mannheim RR station.

Philadelphia

*1. **Atwater-Kent Museum,** 15 South Seventh Street, Philadelphia, PA 19106. (215) 922-3031. Local history museum, open year-round.*

The Atwater-Kent Museum features Philadelphia city history and archaelogy, Victorian doll houses and Philadelphia PCC car 2601 (St. Louis, 1942). In 1996 it mounted a major exhibition on the city's mass transit. "Trains and Trolleys" featured over 300 objects from the museum's collections, a scale model of Broad Street subway station and lectures on city transit history.

*2. **Philadelphia Trolley Coalition,** 616 Carpenter Street, Philadelphia, PA 19147. (215) 755-7717.*

The PTC hopes to "forge a political constituency for the retention, improvement and expansion of the city's streetcar and light rail lines, including those presently operated by buses because of insufficient funds." They also seek to preserve the city's operational street railway and will develop proposals to expand present services, including the historic streetcar loop that served Independence Hall during the 1976 Bicentennial.

*3. **Southeastern Pennsylvania Transportation Authority,** 1234 Market Street, Philadelphia, PA 19107. (215) 574-7300. Standard-gauge commuter rail and rapid transit, 5' 2 1/4" gauge light rail, rapid transit, heritage trolleys, plus ETBs and buses.*

SEPTA is Philadelphia and the Tri-state area's main transit provider. A few PCCs remain: they can't be sold until sufficient time and mileage has accrued since their federally-assisted rebuilding. Some are used in emergencies or on charters, some are painted in older Philadelphia colors for the Chestnut Hill shuttle (which ceased in June, 1996) and "Welcome" trolley line 51. Two center-city tourist lines are proposed; one from Twelfth Street to Penn's Landing via Chestnut and Arch Street, the other on Fourth and Fifth Streets. SEPTA's new headquarters has a museum in which the centerpiece is PCC car 2733 restored to 1947 condition.

A. PCC Cars, March 1996

CAR	BUILDER AND DATE	TRUCK	CAR TYPE
482, 483	St. Louis, unknown	Clark B-2	SE DT PCC Rapid transit cars
(Originally Chicago Transit Authority 6000 class cars. Sold to SEPTA 1987 for Norristown line. In reserve.)			
2054 (1 car)	St. Louis, 1940	Clark B-2	SE DT PCC
2092/98/2105/11/17/18/34/41-43/50/56/58-60/63			
2168/70/71/75/81/82/87/	St. Louis, 1948	Clark B-2	SE DT PCC
90/91/94/96/97 (28 cars)			
2704/11-13/16/17/26/28/30/32/33/38/39/41/46-48/50			
2753/58/60/61/70/77/80/	St. Louis, 1947	Clark B-2	SE DT PCC
83/85/90/96/98/99 (31 cars)			
8042, 8534 (2 cars)	Brill, 1923/1926	Brill 39-E-2	SE DT "Peter Witt" city
(On loan from the Buckingham Valley Trolley Association.)			

By February 1997, less than twenty PCC cars were left on SEPTA property, plus 2160 (a work car), 2187 and 2194 (tower cars). 2054 and 2728 are in 1938 colors, 2168 and 2732 are in 1947 colors, 2799 is in 1949 Philadelphia Suburban colors.

B. Work Cars and Locomotives

07	Jewett, 1911	Unknown	DE DT Line car
(Originally a Philadelphia Suburban freight motor.)			
D-39	Home-built, 1924	Brill 50-E-2	DE DT Line car
W-54, W-56	Brill, 1923	Brill 50-E-2	DE DT drop-side work motor with hoists
W-61, W-62	Unknown	Unknown	Unknown

Pittsburgh

1. Port Authority Transit *Beaver and Island Avenue, Pittsburgh, PA 15233. (412) 237-7000. PCCs run on 5' 2 1/2" gauge Drake line.*

Conversion of PAT's South Hills routes to light rail was completed in 1986 when cars were taken off the Smithfield Street Bridge and city streets and transferred to the new downtown subway and Panhandle Bridge. Mixed light rail and PCC car operation continues, although PCCs are now confined to the Drake route. With the closure of the Overbrook line in 1995, PCCs are no longer seen north of Washington Junction and usually only one operates daily, shuttling between Washington Junction and the Drake loop. Buses are used when maintenance problems prevent a PCC from running. Pittsburgh once had 666 PCCs (one of the largest fleets in North America), operating with hundreds more older cars. The single PCC on the Drake shuttle in 1997 maintains an unbroken sixty years (and counting) of PCC car service to Pittsburgh; a record of longevity unequalled anywhere else. This roster is incomplete.

PCC CARS	BUILDER AND DATE	TRUCK	CAR TYPE
1765	St. Louis, 1949	Clark B-2B	SE DT PCC
4000	Home-built, 1981	St. Louis B-3	SE DT PCC
4001-03	Home-built, 1982	St. Louis B-3	SE DT PCC
4005/06/09	Home-built, 1983/84	St. Louis B-3	SE DT PCC

(4000-class cars have new bodies and other components, plus parts from former 177-class PCC cars.)

2. Senator John Heinz Regional History Center, *1212 Smallman Street Pittsburgh, PA 15222. (412) 454-6000. Museum open year-round.*

This museum has Pittsburgh PCC 1724 (St. Louis, 1949 St. Louis B-3) as a static display, restored to 1949 condition.

3. Spaghetti Warehouse Restaurant, *2601 Smallman Street Pittsburgh, PA 15222.*

The restaurant contains an unidentified Dallas TX car as a dining-room centerpiece. The car was taken out of Dallas service in 1935, and refurbished in 1988.

4. Station Square, *Smithfield and Carson Streets Pittsburgh, PA 15219.*

Station Square has three cars on outdoor display, including Brooklyn convertible 4550, an interurban and a horse car.

Rockhill Furnace

Rockhill Trolley Museum, *run by Railways to Yesterday as the Shade Gap Electric Railway, PO Box 203, Rockhill Furnace, PA 17249. (814) 447-9576. Standard-gauge trolley museum off U.S. 522 at Rockhill Furnace/Orbisonia, 20 miles north of PA turnpike (I-70, I-76) exit 13. Cars run weekends and holidays Memorial Day to end of October 11:30 a.m.-4:30 p.m.*

Cars first ran here in 1962, meeting the narrow-gauge steam trains of the East Broad Top Railroad, one of North America's historical gems and a National Historic Monument. The cars run one mile on a former EBT branch line, some of which retains mixed narrow and standard-gauge tracks for an EBT locomotive reversing wye. Since 1962, the RTM has evolved from a single-car "Toonerville" operation into a museum of Pennsylvania rail transit with a restoration shop and new barns. The EBT roundhouse, unaltered in over a century, is not part of the RTM, but as a neighbor, it is a must-see rail history destination in itself. RTM was recently named a partner in the proposed East Broad Top Trust, a professionally-run a non-profit foundation which will conserve and interpret the EBT and continue its tourist operations. The RTM would help preserve EBT's historic shops and machinery at Rockhill and would itself receive assistance in extending its tracks to US 522, where a remote EBT parking lot would be built. From there, trolleys would shuttle passengers to and from the narrow-gauge steam trains.

A. City and Suburban Cars

CAR	BUILDER AND DATE	TRUCK	CAR TYPE
Lemoyne, (Harrisburg PA) Valley Rys. 12	Jackson & Sharp, 1900	–	DE DT City (body only)

Philadelphia SEPTA (Red Arrow) 23	St. Louis, 1949	St. Louis	DE DT MU suburban PCC
Philadelphia Suburban (Red Arrow) 61	Brill, 1925	Brill 27-MCB-3X	DE DT Center-entrance suburban
Philadelphia SEPTA (P&W) 162	Brill, 1927	Brill 27-MCB-2X	DE DT "Strafford" suburban
York (PA) Rys. 163	Brill, 1924	Brill 77-E-1 (from Japan)	DE DT Curved-side city
(A rare Brill copy of a Cincinnati Car Co. curved-side design.)			
Oporto (Portugal) STCP 172	Home-built, 1929	Brill 21-E	DE ST Semi-convertible
Philadelphia SEPTA (P&W) 205	Brill, 1931	Brill 89-E-2	DE DT "Bullet" lightweight suburban
Oporto (Portugal) STCP 249	Brill, 1904	Belgian Brill 39-E copy	DE DT Semi-convertible
Johnstown (PA) Traction Co. 311	Wason, 1922	Brill 77-E-1	DE DT Birney "safety"
(Originally Bangor [ME] 14.)			
Rio de Janeiro (Brazil) 322	St. Louis, 1906	Brill 21-E (home-made from parts)	DE ST 9-bench open
(Partially restored body destroyed when building housing car was burned. Parts in storage for a possible future restoration.)			
Johnstown (PA) Traction Co. 355	St. Louis, 1926	St. Louis EDJ-64	DE DT Lightweight city
Scranton (PA) Transit Co. 505	Osgood Bradley, 1929	Osgood-Bradley 45/66	DE DT "Electromobile" lightweight city
Harrisburg (PA) Ry. Co 710	Brill, 1914	Brill 27-MCB-1	DE DT City
D. C. Transit (Washington) 1430	St. Louis, 1944	Clark B-2	SE DT PCC
Rio de Janeiro (Brazil) 1875	Home-built, 1912	Unknown	DE DT 13-bench open
Philadelphia SEPTA 2743	St. Louis, 1947	Clark B-2	SE DT PCC
(Existing trucks are being converted to standard-gauge.)			

Philadelphia SEPTA (Red Arrow) 13 and D.C. Transit 1430, were deaccessioned in 1997.

B. Interurban and Electric Freight Cars

Hagerstown & Frederick (MD) 5	Home-built, 1920	Taylor MCB	DE DT Freight motor
Philadelphia SEPTA (P&W) Liberty Liner	St. Louis, 1941	GSI Commonwealth cast steel	DE 4-section articulated "Electroliner"
(Originally Chicago, North Shore and Milwaukee 803/804.)			
Chicago, Aurora & Elgin 315	Kuhlman, 1909	Baldwin 84-35	DE DT Interurban coach
Philadelphia SEPTA (P&W) 402	Detroit United, circa 1920	Standard C-80P	DE DT Work car
(Originally Eastern Michigan Rys. 2010, an interurban box motor.)			

C. Rapid Transit Cars

Philadelphia SEPTA 1009	Brill, 1936	Commonwealth	DE DT "Bridge" subway

D. Work Cars and Locomotives

Capital Transit (DC) 09	McGuire Cummings, 1898	McGuire Cummings pedestal	DE ST Snowsweeper
Philadelphia SEPTA (P&W) 10	Wason, 1915	Wason	DE DT Shear plow
Oporto (Portugal) STCP C-64	Home-built, 1933	Brill 21-E	DE ST Coal car (used as tool car)
Scranton (PA) Transit Co. 107	Chicago & Joliet shops, 1910	Peckham	DE ST Snowsweeper
(Originally a Chicago & Joliet Electric Railway snowsweeper.)			

Wilmington (DE) ETB 623 has been sold to the Seashore Trolley Museum, Kennebunkport, ME. Johnstown Traction ETB 710, (originally Wilmington [DE] 670) has been scrapped. Newport News (VA) bus 314 (Mack 1947) has been donated to a Pittsburgh bus museum.

Washington (Arden)

1. Pennsylvania Railway Museum Association (Pennsylvania Trolley Museum) 1 Museum Road, Washington, PA 15301. (412) 228-9256. 5' 2 1/2" gauge trolley museum on North Main Street extension, two miles north of Washington PA. Cars run daily Memorial Day-Labor Day, weekends April-December, 11:00 a.m.- 5:00 p.m.

In 1940, the Pittsburgh chapter of the NRHS acquired a Pittsburgh trailer body but vandals so damaged it that donating the car to a wartime scrap drive seemed the best course. When peace returned, three members withdrew to form an independent Pittsburgh Electric Railway Club and began to run fantrips. The PERC bought Pittsburgh M-1 in 1949 and two more soon after, storing them in Ingram car house. It located the present site, a 1/2 mile segment of the Pittsburgh Railway's Washington interurban in 1953. The first cars came from Pittsburgh under their own power on February 7th, 1954. They were the last to traverse the now-closed line, cut back to the Allegheny County line (Drake loop) some months before. The PERC became the PRMA in 1960 and cars first ran in June 1963 on the Arden Short Line Electric Railway (now known as the Pennsylvania Trolley Museum). The 1-mile Arden Mines extension, a new line on the bed of an old coal mine railroad, was opened in 1995 and attention has now turned to the interurban line. This will be extended 1/2-mile back towards Pittsburgh to serve the newly acquired museum "east site." Development plans for this 18-acre lot are still being prepared, but will include a new visitor center and a loop near the junction of Country Club Road and North Main Street. A fine new Visitors' Center houses photographic exhibits, interpretive displays and small artifacts. The four passenger waiting shelters at various points on the line, are genuine relics. The 1909 Allison and Richfol shelters are Pittsburgh artifacts, the 1907 Brown Shelter is from the Pittsburgh and Butler Street Ry. and the 1908 West shelter is from the Pittsburgh, Harmony, Butler and New Castle.

A. City and Suburban Cars

CAR	BUILDER AND DATE	TRUCK	CAR TYPE
Philadelphia SEPTA (Red Arrow) 5	Brill, 1941	Brill 89-E-1	DE DT Suburban MU "Brilliner"
Philadelphia SEPTA (Red Arrow) 14/24	St. Louis, 1949	St. Louis	DE DT Suburban MU PCC
Philadelphia Suburban (Red Arrow) 66/73	Brill, 1926	Brill 27-MCB-3X	DE DT Center-entrance suburban
Philadelphia Suburban (Red Arrow) 78	Brill, 1932	Brill 89-E-1	DE DT Lightweight suburban
Cleveland RTA (Shaker Rapid) 94	Pullman-Standard, 1947	Clark B-2	SE DT MU PCC
Philadelphia SEPTA (P&W) 209	Brill, 1931	Brill 89-E-2	DE DT "Bullet" lightweight suburban
Johnstown (PA) Traction Co. 350	St. Louis, 1926	St. Louis EDJ-64	DE DT Lightweight city
New Orleans PSI 832	Perley Thomas, 1922	Brill 76-E-2	DE DT city
Pittsburgh Ry. Co. 1138/1467	St. Louis, 1937/1942	Clark B-2	SE DT PCC
Pittsburgh Ry. Co. 1711	St. Louis, 1949	St. Louis B-3	SE DT PCC
Rio de Janeiro (Brazil) 1774	Home-built, 1912	–	DE DT 13-bench open
Originally owned by the Rockhill Trolley Museum.)			
Pittsburgh PAT 1799 (II)	St. Louis, 1945	Clark B-2	SE DT PCC
(Originally numbered 1640.)			
Philadelphia SEPTA 2723	St. Louis, 1947	Clark B-2	SE DT PCC
Pittsburgh Ry. Co. 3487	St. Louis, 1905	Bemis 45-S	DE DT City
Pittsburgh Ry. Co. 3756	Osgood Bradley, 1925	Unknown	SE DT Low-floor city
Pittsburgh Ry. Co. 4140	Pressed Steel, 1911	Unknown	SE DT Jones high-floor city
(Later became Pittsburgh Ry. Co. M-200.)			
Pittsburgh Ry. Co. 4398	St. Louis, 1916	Unknown	SE DT Low-floor city
Philadelphia PRT 5326	Brill, 1923	Brill 39-E-2	DE DT Lightweight city

Philadelphia SEPTA (Red Arrow) MU suburban PCC 19 was bought for parts. Pittsburgh PAT 1788 [II] (originally 1639) owned by the Pittsburgh History and Landmarks Foundation, was stored at Arden until 1995 when the Foundation sold it to Edward Miller.

B. Interurban and Electric Freight Cars

CAR	BUILDER AND DATE	TRUCK	CAR TYPE
Pittsburgh, Harmony, Butler & New Castle Ry. 115	St. Louis, 1909	–	DE DT Interurban coach (body only)
Monongahela West Penn 274	Jewett, 1918	Brill 27-MCB-2X	DE DT Combine
(Originally Monongahela Valley Traction 274.)			
West Penn Ry. Co. 739	Home-built, 1925	–	DE DT center-entrance interurban coach (body only)
West Penn Ry. Co. 832	Cincinnati, 1930	Cincinnati 101	DE DT Lightweight interurban coach

The body of West Penn Ry. Co. DE DT center-entrance interurban coach 722 (Home-built, 1921) is being used for parts.

C. Work Cars and Locomotives

West Penn Ry. Co. 1	Home-built, 1916	Home-built truck	DE ST Box cab locomotive
Pittsburgh Ry. Co. M-1	Pullman, 1890	Mcguire	DE ST Pay car
(Originally Pittsburgh double-truck car 639. Shortened and single-trucked at unknown date. Pay car circa 1900.)			
Arden (PA) Electric Ry. 2	Brill, 1923	Brill 50-E-2	DE DT overhead line car
(Originally PRT/PTC/SEPTA Snow Sweeper C-125, modified to line car by Pennsylvania trolley museum after acquisition in 1974.)			
Philadelphia SEPTA (Red Arrow) 4	McGuire-Cummings, 1922	Baldwin MCB	DE DT Snow sweeper
Philadelphia SEPTA (Red Arrow) 07	Jewett, 1911	Baldwin MCB	DE DT Freight motor
Philadelphia PRT F-22	Brill, 1913	Brill 50-E	DE DT Milk car
(In 1950 became Philadelphia PTC/SEPTA T-16 and transferred to Market Street-Frankord elevated line as a service car.)			
Pittsburgh Ry. Co. M-37	McGuire, 1896	Mcguire	DE ST Snow sweeper
Pittsburgh Ry. Co. M-56	McGuire-Cummings, 1918	McGuire-Cummings	DE DT Snow sweeper
(Originally Beaver Valley Traction [PA] 1.)			
Columbus (OH) Ry. Pwr. & Lt. 067	Home-built, 1923	Peckham 14B	DE DT Motorized flat car
Pittsburgh PAT M-210	Home-built, 1940	Unknown	DE DT Line car
(This car was built using portions of Pittsburgh low-floor car 4306.)			
Pittsburgh PAT M-283	Differential, 1929	Differential Arch bar	DE DT Crane
Pittsburgh PAT M-551	Differential, 1922	Differential Arch bar	DE DT Side dump car
Monongahela West Penn 3000	Baldwin/WH, 1921	Baldwin (standard-gauge)	DE DT Steeple cab locomotive
Boston MBTA 3618	Differential, 1927	Differential Arch bar	DE DT Bottom dump car

Pittsburgh PAT M-454 (originally 4115, Pressed Steel) was acquired for parts. Pittsburgh PAT M-57 (Brill, 1923, Brill 50-E-2 trucks) DE DT snow plow (originally Philadelphia PRT snow plow E-206, converted to snow sweeper 1927 and renumbered C-145) was traded to SEPTA early in 1997 for SEPTA (Red Arrow) 07.

TENNESSEE

Chattanooga

Chattanooga Choo Choo, *1400 Market Street, Chattanooga, TN 37402. (423) 266-5000. Standard-gauge tourist trolley. Car runs daily year-round.*

Opened in 1973, a half-mile of trolley line circles the Chattanooga Choo Choo complex, an imaginative recycling of the city's railroad station into a hotel, entertainment, retail and leisure center. The track was extended to the Convention Center in 1977, and to another part of the station a little later, but this last extension closed in the late 1980s. Originally New Orleans PSI 952 was used, but this and Rio de Janeiro (Brazil) 13-bench open 1794, bought from the Connecticut Trolley Museum, were sold to New Orleans in the late 1980s. 1794 is now in Memphis. The present Choo Choo 952 is New Orleans 959 (Perley Thomas, 1924)

Memphis

Memphis Area Transit Authority (Main Street Trolley), *1370 Levee Road, Memphis, TN 38108. (901) 722-7100. Standard-gauge tourist trolley. Cars run daily year-round on Main Street, Memphis.*

This 2 1/2 mile line is at the heart of a multi-million dollar downtown revival package. Main Street Trolley is more vintage light rail than tourist trolley. Opened April 29, 1993, MST is a first instalment; the former Illinois Central RR line alongside the Wolf and Mississippi rivers is owned by MATA who are building a trolley line on it, connecting at each end with MST to complete a downtown distributor loop, opening in 1997. Though the Portuguese cars provide most Main Street service, the big Melbourne cars have been successful and several more are being restored by Gomaco for the line. All Oporto cars in service are painted and lettered "Main Street Trolley," but

75

have kept their original numbers. (NIS = unrestored and not yet in service)

CITY CARS	BUILDER AND DATE	TRUCK	CAR TYPE
Oporto (Portugal) CCFP 114 (NIS)	Brill, unknown	Brill 21-E	DE ST Semi-convertible
Oporto (Portugal) CCFP 156	Home-built, 1933	Brill 21-E	DE ST Semi-convertible
Oporto (Portugal) CCFP 157 (NIS)	Home-built, 1933	Brill 21-E	DE ST Semi-convertible
Oporto (Portugal) CCFP 164	Home-built, 1936	Brill 21-E	DE ST Semi-convertible
Oporto (Portugal) CCFP 165/75 (NIS)	Home-built, unknown	Brill 21-E	DE ST Semi-convertible
Oporto (Portugal) CCFP 178 (NIS)	Home-built, 1935	Brill 21-E	DE ST Semi-convertible
Oporto (Portugal) CCFP 180	Home-built, 1935	Brill 21-E	DE ST Semi-convertible
Oporto (Portugal) CCFP 181 (NIS)	Home-built, 1935	Brill 21-E	DE ST Semi-convertible
Oporto (Portugal) CCFP 187	Home-built, unknown	Brill 21-E	DE ST Semi-convertible
Oporto (Portugal) CCFP 188 (NIS)	Home-built, unknown	Brill 21-E	DE ST Semi-convertible
Oporto (Portugal) CCFP 194	Home-built, 1935	Brill 21-E	DE DT Semi-convertible
Oporto (Portugal) CCFP 197 (NIS)	Home-built, 1931	Brill 21-E	DE ST Semi-convertible
Oporto (Portugal) CCFP 204	Home-built, 1940	Brill 21-E	DE ST Semi-convertible
Melbourne (Australia) M&MTB 234	Home-built, 1924	Melbourne Type 1	DE DT Type W2 drop-center
Oporto (Portugal) CCFP 266/68 (NIS)	Home-built, 1930	–	DE DT "Fumista"" Semi-convertible
Melbourne (Australia) M&MTB 417 (NIS)	Home-built, 1926	Melbourne Type 1	DE DT Type W2 drop-center
Melbourne (Australia) M&MTB 503 (NIS)	James Moore, 1928	Melbourne Type 1	DE DT Type W2 drop-center
Melbourne (Australia) M&MTB 539/40 (NIS)	Home-built, 1928	Melbourne Type 1	DE DT Type W2 drop-center
Melbourne (Australia) M&MTB 545	Home-built, 1929	Melbourne Type 1	DE DT Type W2 drop-center
Melbourne (Australia) M&MTB 553 (NIS)	Home-built, 1929	Melbourne Type 1	DE DT Type W2 drop-center
Rio de Janeiro (Brazil) 1794 (NIS)	Home-built, 1914	Unknown	DE DT 13-bench open
(Originally at Connecticut Trolley Museum, to Chattanooga Choo Choo circa 1975, to New Orleans 1989, to Memphis 1996.)			
Gomaco 1978	M&MTB, 1926	Melbourne Type 1	DE DT Type W2 drop-center
(Originally Melbourne [Australia] M&MTB 353 until restored by Gomaco as a demonstrator in 1990.)			
Gomaco 1979	Gomaco, 1993	Modified single Melbourne Type 1	DE ST Replica semi-convertible

TEXAS

Dallas

1. McKinney Avenue Transit Authority, 3153 Oak Grove, Dallas, TX 75204. (214) 855-0006. Standard-gauge tourist trolley runs daily year-round.

The McKinney Avenue project began when local business owners, seeking to link their reviving area with downtown Dallas, found trolley tracks (unused since 1956) under the blacktop of McKinney Avenue. These tracks were the nucleus of the project, supplemented by new-build tracks at each end of the line where it deviates from McKinney Avenue. Service began July 22, 1989. The line will be extended a half-mile at each end to serve the City Place and West End light rail stations.

CAR	BUILDER AND DATE	TRUCK	CAR TYPE
North Texas Traction 322	Home-built, 1912	Unknown	DE DT Box motor
(Originally numbered 32, this car is being rebuilt by McKinney Avenue as an interurban parlor/diner.)			
McKinney Avenue 122	Brill, 1909	Brill 21-E	DE ST Semi-convertible
(Originally Oporto [Portugal] CCFP 122.)			
Dallas Railway & Terminal 183/86/89	St. Louis, 1913	Melbourne Type 1 (186 only)	DE DT Stone & Webster city (body only 183/89)

Dallas Railway & Terminal 323	American, 1914	–	DE DT Stone & Webster city (body only)
McKinney Avenue 369 (Originally Melbourne [Australia] M&MTB 369.)	James Moore, 1925	Melbourne Type 1	DE DT Type W2 drop-center
Dallas Railway & Terminal 636	Brill, 1920	Modified single Melbourne Type 1	DE ST Birney "safety"
Dallas Railway & Terminal 754	American, 1926	–	SE DT "Peter Witt" city (body only)
Toronto TTC 4613/14 (Toronto cars originally Type A-8 4503/09 stored at Dallas DART light rail shops.)	St. Louis/CCF, 1951	Clark B-2	SE DT Type A-15 PCC

Dallas 754 is at Gomaco of Ida Grove IA for restoration. Dallas 183 and 189 will also be sent to Gomaco for restoration. The restoration of Dallas 323 is not yet planned. There are no current plans to acquire any surviving Dallas double-end PCC cars.

2. Age of Steam RR Museum. *Southwest Railroad Historical Society, PO Box 26369, Dallas, TX 75226-0369. (214) 421-8754. Open weekends all year 11:00 a.m.- 5:00 p.m.*

This is a static museum of railroad locomotives, passenger and freight equipment located at the north side of Fair Park (the Texas State fairgrounds). The display includes Boston MBTA PCC 3329 (Pullman, 1945, originally Dallas Railway & Terminal 624).

El Paso

Paseo Del Norte Streetcar Preservation Society, c/o Ron Dawson, 3300 Montana (rear), El Paso, TX 79903 or 6716 Stone Court El Paso, TX 79924. Streetcar preservation group, proposed tourist trolley. Cars not on public display.

The PDNSPS began in the mid-1980s when El Paso's 17 former San Diego PCC cars (stored since the line closed in 1974) were evicted from their carhouse, due to be converted into a firehouse. Those cars kept outside were scrapped, but the nine cars kept inside were bought by the PDNSPS, plus El Paso "Stone & Webster" city car body 90. Plans for their possible use include a revival of the old line on the U.S. side of the border, or a heritage line in downtown El Paso. Progress has stalled since 1990, although a fundraising calendar is published annually and the cars are protected. One or more PCC cars may be sold to raise seed money.

Fort Worth

1. Fort Worth Transportation Authority, *PO Box 1477, Fort Worth, TX 76101-1477. Cars not on public display.*

Northern Texas Traction interurban coaches 25 and 411 (St. Louis 1913, 1919), ran between Fort Worth and Dallas until 1934, when they were sold for use as a lake house at Eagle Mountain Lake. In May 1995 they went to Fort Worth's Texas and Pacific RR station for restoration and static display, in connection with the station's remodeling into a multi-modal transportation center. Plans exist to set up a not-for-profit foundation to raise money to pay for the restoration. An ongoing effort to revitalize and beautify the area around the T&P station is spawning plans by the FWTA to instal a heritage trolley line connecting with the Tandy subway. As part of the redevelopment, I-30 is to be moved to the south, away from the station.

2. Tandy Subway Tandy Corporation, *One Tandy Center, Fort Worth, TX 76102. (817) 390-3700. Standard-gauge vintage light rail. Cars run daily year-round.*

The mile-long Tandy line was built by the Leonard Brothers to link their downtown department store with a 23-acre parking lot by the Trinity River. Opened in 1963, the line includes 1400 feet of cut-and-cover subway. The Tandy Corporation bought the store 1967, demolished it and substituted the present Tandy Center. The line was unaltered, its basement terminal serving the Center's shopping mall and office block, plus the surrounding downtown area.

CARS	BUILDER AND DATE	TRUCK	CAR TYPE
1 (II) (Originally Boston MBTA 3168)	Pullman-Standard, 1945	Clark B-2	DE DT rebuilt PCC
2 (Originally DC Transit 1551)	St. Louis, 1945	Clark B-2	DE DT rebuilt PCC
3 (Originally DC Transit 1535)	St. Louis, 1945	Clark B-2	DE DT rebuilt PCC
4 (Originally DC Transit 1506)	St. Louis, 1945	Clark B-2	DE DT rebuilt PCC
5 (Originally DC Transit 1541)	St. Louis, 1945	Clark B-2	DE DT rebuilt PCC
6 (II) (Originally DC Transit 1536)	St. Louis, 1945	Clark B-2	DE DT rebuilt PCC

| 7 (Originally DC Transit 1205) | St. Louis, 1939 | Clark B-2 | DE DT rebuilt PCC |
| 8 (Originally DC Transit 1200) | St. Louis, 1939 | Clark B-2 | DE DT rebuilt PCC |

All cars in service from 1962 were recognizably PCCs, with additional streamlining and decorations. Those remaining in service during 1977/78 were remodelled to the present configuration except for 6 (I) (originally DC Transit 1540) which was sold out of service and ended up as a bodyshell in Arkansas before acquisition by the National Capital Trolley Museum where it awaits restoration. Several other PCC cars were purchased from Boston in the 1970s, but all except one were used for parts.

Galveston

Galveston Park Board of Trustees, *823 Roseberg Street, Galveston TX 77550. Standard-gauge tourist trolley. Cars run daily year-round.*

A turn-of-the century boom town, rich in buildings of every style from ante-bellum to Art Deco, Galveston suffered decades of decline following the devasting hurricane of 1901 and commercial development passed it by so that the city today has the largest and most diverse collection of surviving Victorian buildings anywhere in North America. Whole neighborhoods became fashionable again in the 1980s, including the Strand (close to downtown), and Seawall (by the beaches 4 1/2 miles away). The city believed a tourist trolley should link the two: a user-friendly alternative to automobiles. Opened in 1988, the line is unwired for fear that hurricanes would blow them down, leaving the city vulnerable to lawsuits. Cars 1-4 are diesel-electrics, built in 1987 by Miner Car on modified Bettendorf freight car trucks. The cars resemble Brill double-end double-truck semi-convertibles of 1903-1919.

Plano

Haggard Park, *East 15th and H Streets, Plano, TX 75074. Museum open Saturday afternoons year-round.*

The park houses a museum of Texas Electric artifacts in the former Texas Electric Plano station, 20 miles north of downtown Dallas. Texas Electric 360 (American, 1911), an RPO car on former South Shore Baldwin 84-60AA trucks, sits outside the station.

San Antonio

1. **San Antonio Car Company**-*see San Antonio Museum Association.*

The San Antonio Car Company owns and restores historic streetcars. Its first restoration was San Antonio 300 (American, 1907), completed in 1981 for the San Antonio Museum Association. The four cars listed are either being restored or will be restored by this group for possible operation on the Texas Transportation Company's Pearl Brewery trackage.

CITY CARS	BUILDER AND DATE	TRUCK	CAR TYPE
San Antonio, Alamo Heights 111 (probably) *(Originally an open car.)*	Unknown builder circa 1898	–	DE ST City (body only)
San Antonio PS 205	American, 1905	–	DE DT City (body only)
San Antonio PS 257	American, 1911	–	DE DT City (body only)
San Antonio PS 314	American, 1914	–	DE DT City (body only)

2. **San Antonio Museum Association,** *PO Box 2601, San Antonio, TX 78229-2601. (210) 820-2111.*

The San Antonio Museum Association completed the restoration of the vacant Lone Star brewery as an art museum in 1981. The brewery was served by a spur of the Texas Transportation Company until the mid-1950s and the spur was re-electrified in 1981 to store newly-restored car 300 (American, 1913). Owned by the SAMA since 1933, it was originally a 4' gauge single-end car. SAMA volunteers, in conjunction with the San Antonio Car Company, rebuilt it as a double-end standard-gauge car. Car 300 was in service between 1982 and 1985 on Pearl Brewery trackage, but fiscal cuts and insurance problems put a stop to its outings and in 1990 it was leased to Gales Creek Enterprises of Oregon for use on Portland's Lake Oswego (Willamette Shore trolley) line. GCE's operating lease for Lake Oswego expired in 1995 and the car is stored on their property in Oregon. The SAMA also owns San Antonio PS bus 21 (Fageol, 1923).

3. Texas Transportation Company, *312 Pearl Parkway, San Antonio, TX 78215. (210) 226-0231. Standard-gauge trolley freight line, irregularly-scheduled operation.*

The Texas Transportation Company operates a downtown network of electrified switching lines belonging to the Pearl Brewery, which interchanges with the railroads via Jones Avenue. Electric switching continues, but conversion to diesel traction is imminent.

LOCOMOTIVE	BUILDER AND DATE	TRUCK	CAR TYPE
Texas Transportation Co. 1	Baldwin/WH, 1917	Baldwin MCB	DE DT Type B Locomotive
(Originally Monongahela West Penn 3002, then Kansas City & Kaw Valley RR 504. Sold to Pearl Brewery in 1954.)			
Texas Transportation Co. 2	Texas Electric, 1929	Unknown	DE DT Type C Locomotive
(Originally Texas Traction Co. interurban 4 [St. Louis, 1907], became Texas Electric 351 in 1917. Rebuilt as a locomotive in 1929 and renumbered 952, sold to Pearl Brewery in 1949.)			

Van Alstyne

City Parks Department, *PO Box 1702, Van Alstyne, TX 75495.*

The bodies of Texas Electric box motor 501 and a box trailer, on a farm in North Plano for almost fifty years, were donated to Van Alstyne (north of Plano) during 1996. The city parks department will restore them for static display.

VIRGINIA

Roanoke

Virginia Museum of Transportation, *Norfolk Avenue SW, Roanoke, VA 24016. (703) 342-5670. Rail museum, open daily 10:00 a.m.-5:00 p.m. except Thanksgiving, Christmas and New Year's Day.*

Named the official transportation museum of the Commonwealth of Virginia in 1983 because of the diversity and range of its collections, the VMT has a substantial automotive collection, DC Transit PCC car 1470 (St. Louis, 1945), an unidentified Roanoke car and a Safety Motor Transit Lines (Roanoke) 1947 Mack C41 GT bus.

WASHINGTON

Lynnwood

City of Lynnwood Parks Department, *Lynnwood, WA 98036. (206) 771-4030.*

Lynnwood Parks Department is cosmetically restoring Pacific Northwest Traction Company (North Coast Lines) Seattle-Everett interurban coach 55 (Niles, 1910) for possible display at a site adjacent to the old right-of-way in Lynnwood, which is now a footpath. The car was for many years a ticket office at the Puget Sound and Snoqualmie Valley Railroad in Snoqualmie, WA.

Seattle

1. Museum of History and Industry, *2700 24th Avenue E., Seattle, WA 98112. (206) 324-1125.*

The Museum of History and Industry (just south of Husky Stadium) traces Seattle, King County and Pacific Northwest history. A 3/4-scale 1880s street scene is featured. The MHI owns Seattle Cable Railway car 13 (Stockton, circa 1888) but has not displayed it for some time and no funds are available in the immediate future for its restoration and return to public display.

2. King County Metro, *821 Second Avenue, Seattle, WA. 98104. (206) 553-3000.*

King County Metro (until recently known as Seattle Metro) is Seattle's transit provider with an ETB, dual-purpose ETB/motor bus and motor bus route network. It also owns and operates the

Waterfront streetcar tourist trolley (see below) plus the Alweg monorail, installed for the 1962 Seattle World's Fair, which runs from the fairgrounds at Seattle Center to Westlake (downtown). The 1.3-mile ETB subway opened in 1990. Rare in North American practice, only the Boston area currently has anything similar: the Cambridge/Harvard Square tunnel which was converted from streetcar to ETB operation in 1958. More unusual still are the light rail tracks in the Seattle ETB tunnel, ready for use should the voters decide to instal a system. The stations are large, beautifully-decorated architectural showpieces. When the tunnel was built, the monorail was extended a few hundred feet to a new station on the second floor of a shopping mall, with the Westlake ETB tunnel station in its basement. This provides an all-weather transfer between the monorail and the rest of Seattle's transit network. A small historical display on Seattle's cable car system (which closed in 1940) is on the south mezzanine of Pioneer Square ETB subway tunnel station. It includes a "bull" wheel which turned the Yesler way cable rope around at the downtown terminal.

3. ***Metro Employees Historic Vehicle Association,*** *c/o King County Metro, 821 Second Avenue, Seattle, WA 98104-1598. MEHVA hotline (206) 633-4590. Museum collection not on public view, but several trips on vintage ETBs and motor buses from the collection are scheduled annually, leaving from Second Avenue and South Main Street, across from Seattle's Fire department headquarters. The vintage buses can also be chartered.*

The MEHVA is a volunteer group preserving Seattle and King County's transit heritage "by restoring and operating vintage transit vehicles as a working, living museum." It was started in 1981 by METRO employees anxious to preserve some pre-World War II ETBs, recently taken out of service, and soon began a working relationship with METRO, the city's municipal transit operator. This relationship was formalized in 1984 when Metro Council established a museum bus fleet and recognized MEHVA as its curator. Metro provides storage space, maintenance facitlities and insurance, MEHVA restores, maintains and operates the buses, supplies parts not in Metro stock and reimburses Metro on a per-mile basis for electricity, fuel and tires. MEHVA members are Metro employees but the work they do for MEHVA is done on their own time, without pay.

In the mid-1980s, MEHVA began operating some of the old buses on public excursions. ETB trips are confined to Seattle, the buses go out to the Cascades, Snohomish, Cedar Falls and other destinations. Occasionally a trip will explore some aspect of King County history-a 1996 excursion traced the route of the former Puget Sound Electric Railway's Seattle-Tacoma interurban (1902-1928). Other MEHVA activities include organized work parties, picnics, fan trips, an annual banquet and illustrated talks on local transit history.

A. City Car

CAR	BUILDER AND DATE	TRUCK	CAR TYPE
Seattle MUNI 210	American, 1918	–	DE ST Birney "safety" (body only)

(This car is to be cosmetically restored, but ultimately it is hoped to put it into operating condition for use on the Waterfront Streetcar line.)

B. Electric Trolley Buses

BUS	BUILDER AND DATE	SERIAL NUMBER
Seattle Metro 636 (originally 955)	Twin Coach 44GTT, 1943	78083
Seattle Metro 643	Twin Coach 40GWFT, 1940	75239
Seattle Metro 798	Pacific Car & Foundry/Brill 40SMT, 1940	679
Seattle Metro 1005 (became 655 in 1974)	Pullman-Standard 44CX, 1944	5527

C. Motor Buses

Island Transit (King County WA) 48	GM TDH-3610, 1948	– (Diesel)
(This bus operated on Vashon Island and is jointly owned with the Vashon Parks District.)		
Suburban TS (King County WA) 82	Kenworth K-10, 1947	– (Gasoline)
(Kenworth built only fifteen buses of this type.)		
Seattle Transit System 172	Win Coach 41S, 1948	1049 (Gasoline)
Seattle Transit System 263	GM TDH-5105, 1955	1579 (Diesel)
Seattle Transit System 598	Flxible F2D6V-401-1, 1963	51830 (Diesel)
Seattle Transit System 724	GM T8H-5305, 1968	025 (Diesel)
Seattle Metro 1122	AM General 10240B, 1976	00363 (Diesel)
Seattle Transit System 1705	Kenworth H-30, 1938	50355 (body only)
Seattle Metro 2962	GM TDH-4512, 1959	3088 (Diesel)

A King County Metro 1400-class MAN/AM General articulated bus (1978), will be acquired as the type is phased out of service in 1997.

3. Old Spaghetti Factory Restaurant, *2801 Elliott Avenue Seattle, WA 98121. (206) 441-7724.*

The restaurant has Puget Sound Traction Light & Power (Bellingham, WA) Birney "safety" car body 360 (St. Louis, 1917) as a dining-room center piece.

4. Waterfront Streetcar *King County Metro, 821 Second Avenue, Seattle, WA 98104. (206) 553-3000. Standard-gauge tourist trolley. Cars run daily year-round.*

This was the first new-build stand-alone tourist trolley in the West. It was proposed in 1974 by Seattle councilman George Benson who saw it as a foundation on which to base the restoration of Seattle's waterfront. He has gone to bat for it ever since. The 11/4-mile line, on Alaskan Way between Broad and Jackson, opened May 29, 1982 as Seattle Metro's route 99. With high-platform stations and handicapped access, route 99 is in fact a vintage light rail line. A 1/2-mile extension opened in 1987 from Alaskan Way along Main Street via Pioneer Square to Fifth and Jackson at the ETB tunnel entrance in the International District.

CITY CAR	BUILDER AND DATE	TRUCK	CAR TYPE
Melbourne (Australia) M&MTB 272	James Moore, 1925	Melbourne Type 1	DE DT Type W2 drop-center city
Melbourne (Australia) M&MTB 482	Home-built, 1928	Melbourne Type 1	DE DT Type W2 drop-center city
Melbourne (Australia) M&MTB 512/18	James Moore, 1928	Melbourne Type 1	DE DT Type W2 drop-center city
Melbourne (Australia) M&MTB 605	Home-built, 1930	Melbourne Type 1	DE DT Type W2 drop-center city

(Melbourne (Australia) M&MTB 525 [home-built 1928] was acquired for parts.)

Yakima

Yakima Electric Railway Museum, *PO Box 649, Yakima, WA 98907-0649. (509) 575-1700. Standard-gauge tourist trolley runs weekends May-October 10:00 a.m.-4:00 p.m, 7:00 p.m. trip Fridays in July and August. Board cars at Third and Pine in Yakima.*

Tourist operations on this former trolley freight system (owned by the Union Pacific RR) began in 1974 as a Bicentennial project. Two Oporto cars, similar to Yakima's early city cars, were imported for the service. The system was largely intact and the cars covered most of it in tourist service. In 1985, two of the three lines closed and UP donated the surviving Selah line to the city. It was put on the National Register of Historic Places in 1991. The YERM (then known as Yakima Interurban Trolley Lines) continued to maintain tourist services. In 1989, Yakima 21 and 22 joined the fleet on a long lease from Robert Hively. Bought in 1930 as a three-car modernization package, they helped Yakima Valley Transportation Company's city lines survive until 1947. One is in service, the other needs restoration. They were bought outright from the Hively family in 1996. A 1994 city-funded study of the line (cut back to the Selah boundary from Selah Civic center and the packing houses in 1993) suggests rehabilitation of the line into an operating trolley museum. ISTEA money is being sought to begin the job. Matching funds will come from the city and the YERM.

A. City Cars

CARS	BUILDER AND DATE	TRUCK	CAR TYPE
Yakima Valley Transportation Co. 21/22	American, 1930	Brill 177-E-1X	DE DT "Master Unit" lightweight city
(These cars later became Portland [OR] Traction 4009, 4010, bought 1958 by Robert Hively and kept at the Puget Sound Historical RR Association's Snoqualmie museum. Car 20 of this trio remains at Snoqualmie in poor condition.)			
Yakima 1776, 1976	CCFP, 1928	Brill 21-E	DE ST Semi-convertible
(Originally Oporto [Portugal] CCFP 254, 260)			

B. Work Cars and Locomotives

Union Pacific RR, Yakima VT 298	GE, 1922	Alco RM63B	DE DT Steeple cab locomotive
Union Pacific RR, Yakima VT "A"	Niles, 1909	Standard C-50	DE DT Line car

Appleton

Trolley car '86, *PO Box 2191, Appleton, WI 54913. Proposed standard-gauge tourist trolley.*

This group was formed to restore Milwaukee TMERL car 846 (St. Louis, 1920, TMERL M35BB trucks) for Appleton's 1986 centennial of electric trolley operation but only now is the restoration nearing completion. Since 1983, the group has owned similar TMERL car 978 (St. Louis, 1928, St. Louis EIB 64 trucks). This actually operated in Appleton during 1983 on a few hundred feet of wired tracks before being sent to San Francisco's first Trolleyfest later in the year. A shipping mishap broke the car's back en route. It did not operate there and after spending some time on display, it was shipped back to Appleton to await the attention of the Trolley car '86 restoration team. Neither car is presently on public display. The plan is to operate one car (and later on, both) on a tourist line in Appleton. An ongoing civic restoration project around the Fox River downtown envisages 1 1/2 miles of bicycle path and trolley route to a city park, using private right-of-way on Wisconsin Central railroad tracks. The city and Trolley Car '86 had hoped to get ISTEA money to kick-start the project. Funds from other sources are now being actively solicited.

East Troy

East Troy Electric Railroad (Wisconsin Trolley Museum), *PO Box 436, East Troy, WI 53120. (414) 548-3837. Standard-gauge trolley, trolley freight and interurban museum. Passenger cars make four round trips on weekends from Memorial Day weekend to the end of October. Board cars at 2002 Church Street, East Troy and at the "Elegant Farmer," Mukwanago.*

In addition to street railways, the Milwaukee Electric Railway & Light Co. had a network of interurban lines radiating from the city. In 1928, a four-track rapid transit westbound exit to the city was built, shared by streetcars and interurbans. The Depression and increased motor traffic shortened the life of the interurbans and the 36-mile Milwaukee to Hales Corners, Mukwanago and East Troy line was cut back to Hales Corners in 1939. The Hales Corners segment ran until 1951, the high speed exit (and entry) to Milwaukee until 1958, when it was replaced by an interstate highway. The village of East Troy, without other rail links, bought the seven-mile segment from the village to the Soo line railroad interchange at Mukwanago. TMERL (and its successors) operated it under contract but later the village took over and by the early 1970s ran a diesel locomotive. In 1972, weekend passenger service to the "Elegant Farmer" at Phantom Lake began, run by a tenant group who brought in several cars.

The village sold the line in 1995 to the Wisconsin Trolley Museum (then the current tenant). Museum operations continue and in addition to passenger traffic, (the electric dining-car runs in particular have been enormously successful, afternoon runs have been added to the evening schedules and a third South Shore car may be converted) a major push is being made to keep existing commercial freight customers (over 250 cars move over the line annually) and attract others. For example, an unwired 1969 extension into Trent Tube, a long-time customer, was wired and formally opened for electric operation on May 4, 1996.

ISTEA money for track rebuilding was awarded in 1993 and work began in 1996. Plans are now finalized for a new visitors center on a four-acre tract owned by the museum at Phantom Woods (the intersection of county roads ES and J). Additionally, an extension to the existing East Troy car barn will double the sheltered accomodation available for the museum fleet, which is currently being acquired by the museum from its present owner, Paul Averdung. East Troy offers the longest ride of any North American trolley or interurban museum on tracks which have been continuously under wire since 1907.

A. City and Suburban Cars

CAR	BUILDER AND DATE	TRUCK	CAR TYPE
LaCrosse (WI) Mississippi Valley PSC 12	St. Louis, 1926	–	DE ST Birney "safety" (body only)
East Troy Electric RR 21	Wisconsin Trolley Museum, 1978	Brill 21-E	DE ST Replica 9-bench open
Philadelphia SEPTA (P&W) 164	Brill, 1927	Brill 27-MCB-2X	DE DT "Strafford" suburban

Milwaukee TMERL 200	Jones, 1887	–	DE ST Parlor (body only)
(Originally a horsecar, became an electric parlor car in 1892, hospital car 400 in 1907, work car 8 in 1919.)			
Duluth-Superior Traction Co. 253	TCRT, 1912	Brill 27-E	DE DT City
(Originally Twin Cities RT 1583.)			
Philadelphia SEPTA 2120, 2185	St. Louis, 1948	Clark B-2	SE DT PCC
(Trucks are standard-gauge versions from Chicago which replaced similar 5' 2 1/4" gauge units from Philadelphia.)			
Toronto TTC 4617	St. Louis/CCF 1951	St. Louis B-3	SE DT Type A-15 PCC
(Originally Toronto TTC Type A-8 4539.)			

B. Interurban and Electric Freight Cars

Chicago, South Shore & South Bend 9/11	Pullman, 1926	Baldwin 84-60	DE DT Interurban coach
Chicago, South Shore & South Bend 24	Pullman, 1927	Baldwin 84-60	DE DT Interurban coach
(Rebuilt by the museum as diner "Beverly Shores.")			
Chicago, South Shore & South Bend 25	Pullman, 1927	Baldwin 84-60	DE DT Interurban coach
(Rebuilt by the museum as diner "Ravenswood.")			
Sheboygan (WI) Light & Power 27	Cincinnati, 1908	–	DE DT Interurban coach (body only)
Chicago, South Shore & South Bend 30	Standard, 1929	Baldwin 84-60	DE DT Interurban coach
Green Bay (WI) Traction Co. 103	Niles, 1903	–	DE DT Interurban coach (body only)
(Later became Wisconsin PS 103.)			
Chicago, South Shore & South Bend 111	Pullman, 1926	Baldwin 84-60	DE DT Combine
Chicago, North Shore & Milwaukee 228	Cincinnati, 1922	Baldwin 84-30AA	DE DT Express motor

C. Rapid Transit Cars

Chicago CTA 4420/53	Cincinnati, 1924	Baldwin 78-30	DE DT Elevated

Boston MBTA rapid transit car 0506 (Pullman, 1923) has been acquired for parts.

D. Work Cars and Locomotives

Milwaukee TMERL L6	St. Louis, 1911	St. Louis 47	DE DT Utility crane
Milwaukee TMERL L8	Home-built, 1935	TMERL 100AB	DE DT Steeple-cab locomotive
East Troy (Milwaukee) L9	Home-built, 1944	MERL 100AB	DE DT Steeple-cab locomotive
Milwaukee TMERL L23	Home-built, 1907,	Unknown rebuilt circa 1929	DE DT Overhead line car

Kenosha

In 1996 Kenosha received $56,000 from Wisconsin's Local Government Grant program and $76,000 of federal money distributed by the Wisconsin through its Congestion Mitigation Air Quality program. The city plans a tourist trolley as a downtown distributor. It will use the money to buy five ex-Toronto PCC cars from VESCO of Windber PA. to kick-start the project. A mile of track will run from the Union Pacific (formerly Chicago and Northwestern) railroad station through downtown to the lakefront.

Milwaukee

Wisconsin Electric Power Company, *231 West Michigan Street Milwaukee, WI 53203. (414) 221-2345.*

WEPCO succeeded TMERL, provider of street railway, interurban, bus and electric power in Milwaukee and south-east Wisconsin in the first half of the 20th century. WEPCO owns Milwaukee, Cream City Railroad horse car 17 (Stephenson, circa 1881) and displayed it in the 1940s at its corporate headquarters. WEPCO is restoring the former interurban station (now the Public Service Building) at 231 West Michigan as its new corporate headquarters and will display the restored car there.

Boston PCC car 3265 is one of the very few of its kind still in regular transit service. It is seen on the turning loop in Ashmont Station ready for another trip to Mattapan on June 1, 1994.

A two-car train of Chicago, Aurora and Elgin interurban cars at the beautifully-manicured Brookins Museum (Trolleyville) in Olmsted Falls, Ohio on May 21, 1995.

Edmonton car 42 on Fort Edmonton Park's 1905 Street on September 15, 1989.

East Troy Electric Railroad ex-Chicago, South Shore & South Bend interurban car 1130 at the grain elevators behind the "Elegant Farmer," at Phantom Woods on May 15, 1994.

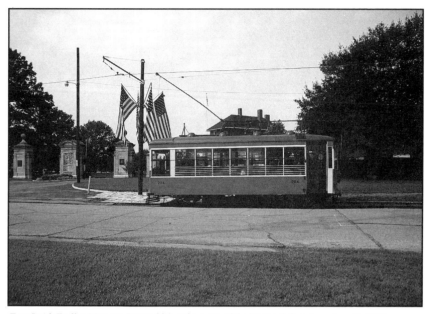

Fort Smith Trolley Museum Birney 224 at the gates of the National Cemetery, June 3, 1995.

Baltimore Trolley Museum's Baltimore open car 1164 rumbles along Falls Road on its way back to the Visitor's Center during April 1983. The creek on the right periodically floods the museum.

DORMANT OR RECENTLY DEFUNCT
COLLECTIONS AND OPERATIONS

CALIFORNIA

Long Beach   *Richard J. Fellows private collection.*

Richard Fellows (1936-1995) was the son of the Fellows and Stewart Shipyard's owner. Sited on Terminal Island (between San Pedro and Long Beach), the yard was next door to National Metals, which in the 1950s had the scrapping contract for cars of Los Angeles and Pacific Electric. Fellows loved the PE and was uniquely placed to rescue cars and hardware from National Metals since its owner was a family friend. Fellows subsequently donated the body of PE "Blimp" 457 to the Western Railway Museum at Rio Vista Junction CA., keeping the rest for his private collection. Of these, PE Tower car 00161 was to have been rebuilt as a box motor, but Fellows in 1971 donated it to the Seal Beach Historical Society where it now forms part of their heritage museum.

Fellows restored the body of PE 963 (originally 701, St. Louis, 1907), mounted it on a motorized rubber-tired chassis and from the 1960s used it as a mobile display in parades. More recently it could be seen at ground-breaking and opening ceremonies for the Los Angeles light rail line, replicating PE's 1001-1057 class (Jewett, 1913) and given the number 1058. It featured in several movies, including the Woody Guthrie biopic "Bound for Glory" and Disney's "Who Framed Roger Rabbit?" Fellows intended to restore the other cars similarly, but he died in September 1995 and the work was never completed. His collection was auctioned at the end of February 1996, the Orange Empire Railway Museum (of which he was a life-long member) acquiring 524 and 993. Mrs. Fellows subsequently donated the body of PE 655 (St. Louis, 1924), a "Hollywood" suburban car to the museum. PE 1058 is unsold at the time of writing.

Pasadena

In 1983, the Original Downtown Pasadena Company issued a report recommending a 1.5 mile six-car tourist trolley line be built from Colorado Boulevard and Los Robles, south on Los Robles, one block over to Green then west on Green to Raymond, terminating in a multi-street loop encompassing Raymond, Union, DeLacey and Green. The run-down area within the loop would be restored as "The Marketplace," a Victorian-styled retail development with shops, a hotel and a micro-brewery. A 3000' Los Robles to Lake extension was also suggested, the complete project linking two commercial districts. In 1984, ODPC quietly acquired the property needed for "The Marketplace" while John P. Wilson (the promoter) bought six cars from Lisbon. One was cosmetically restored and displayed. Though three cars arrived in 1985, it's not known if all six made it to these shores. The city of Pasadena had reservations about ODPC's ability to raise capital and doubted it was possible to underwrite trolley operations solely out of rental income derived from the development's retail stores. The plan was dormant by 1988. It is not known which cars were bought and where they are now.

FLORIDA

Orlando

1. ***Grand Cypress Resort,*** *60 Grand Cypress Blvd., Orlando, FL 32836. (407) 239-4600. Standard-gauge tourist trolley.*

This resort's line (opened in 1985) was an internal transportation system for visitors and guests, themed as a nostalgic return to turn-of-the-century days. It used vintage cars from (and restored by) the Brussels (Belgium) transit operator. In recent years, track maintenance and the widening of a county road crossed by the line caused out-of-season closures, some lasting over a year, while the line north of the crossing was formally abandoned in June, 1996. It is doubtful the rest of the line will ever re-open since all but one of the cars had been sold by the end of 1996.

CAR	BUILDER AND DATE	TRUCKS	CAR TYPE
Brussels (Belgium) MIVB/STIB 104 8	AM de Nivelles, 1906	Brussels Brill 21-E	DE ST City
Bruseels (Belgium) MIVB/STIB 1069	AM de Nivelles, 1907	Brussels Brill 21-E	DE ST City
Brussels (Belgium) MIVB/STIB 1245	Ateliers d'Haird, 1907	Brussels Brill 21-E	DE ST City
Brussels (Belgium) MIVB/STIB 2190	AM de Nivelles, 1913	Pedestal	DE ST Trailer

2. Orlando Street Car, *(OSCAR) City of Orlando Downtown Development Board, 100 South Orange Avenue, Orlando, FL 32801. (407) 246-3625.*

This was a proposal for a 2.7 mile city-sponsored tourist trolley linking two parking lots, a commercial retail development and downtown shopping streets. UMTA/FTA funding was sought in 1992 and the city acquired former Rio de Janeiro (Brazil) 13-bench open 1889 (home-built, 1912) for the line, one of 12 imported by the Association of Railway Museums in 1965 and initially owned by the Magee museum in Bloomsburg PA as Magee Shortline 3. That museum closed after hurricane-related flooding and the subsequent death of its chief sponsor in 1972 and its equipment was sold. From 1975 to 1992 Magee 3 was displayed in Sarasota FL by the Lionel Train Museum who repainted it as Atlantic City and Shore RR 6843. The car spent some years on the Grand Cypress line in the early 1990s before coming to the city, where it became Orlando 1. It was to have been the line's historic centerpiece: the city bringing in other trolleys for basic services. By March 1996, fiscal pressures had completely changed the project's character. Now known as LYMMO, the system will be run by compressed natural gas-fueled buses on downtown bus-only lanes. The project will cost $21 million and the FTA will provide a 50% match. Construction began in April 1996. The future of the ex-Rio car is undecided.

INDIANA

Chesterton

Chesterton Station Eatery, *301 Grant Avenue, Chesterton, IN 46304. This restaurant was located by the former New York Central Railroad's main line.*

This restaurant, with former South Shore cars, closed in 1995 after the death of its owner. In 1996 a copy shop opened in the former restaurant premises and the cars' former Chicago, South Shore and South Bend paint scheme was replaced by a two-tone gray similar to that of the old New York Central Railroad. Their long-term future, however, is unclear.

INTERURBAN CARS	BUILDER AND DATE	TRUCKS	CAR TYPE
Chicago, South Shore & South Bend 17	Pullman, 1927	Baldwin 84-60AA	DE DT Interurban coach
Chicago, South Shore & South Bend 26	Standard, 1929	Baldwin 84-60AA	DE DT Interurban coach
Chicago, South Shore & South Bend 100/04	Pullman, 1926/7	Baldwin 84-60AA	DE DT Combine

French Lick

Springs Valley Electric Railway, *PO Box 150, French Lick, IN 47432. (812) 936-2405. Standard-gauge tourist trolley.*

The Indiana Railway Museum is a not-for-profit organization founded in 1961 to "secure, preserve, restore display and operate historic railway equipment." In 1978, French Lick became its first permanent home. Facilities include a 1907 limestone-built passenger station, and sixteen miles of former Southern RR track over which the museum began operating the French Lick, West Baden and Southern Railway in 1978 as a recreation of a 1920s railroad branch line. The SVER was added in 1984 to replicate the 1-mile French Lick and West Baden Springs trolley that ran between the two villages between 1903 and 1919. Oporto CCFP "Fumista" single truck semi-convertible car 313 (home-built, 1930) was used, acquired from a defunct line in Toledo, OH. The car was sidelined with a motor fault in 1990. Electric services have not run since though trolley wires were still up in October, 1996. The car is housed in a barn, but Chicago, South Shore and South Bend interurban trailer coaches 204 and 206 are in outdoor storage on the property.

Keokuk

Trans-Mississippi Trolley Co., *200 Water Street, Keokuk, IA 52632. (319) 524-2085. Standard-gauge tourist trolley.*

Keokuk's otherwise unremarkable small-town street railway system had a notable interstate suburban line to Warsaw IL. which crossed the Mississippi River on the Keokuk-Hamilton Bridge Company's double-deck bridge. Rather than use the top (road) deck, the street railway company instead electrified the track on the railroad (lower) deck of the bridge. At Hamilton Junction the trolley line shared tracks with the steam-operated Wabash RR and the Toledo, Peoria & Western RR, providing electric car service as far as Warsaw IL. A second trolley line on the Illinois side ran north from Hamilton Junction to Hamilton, connecting with the eastern end of a trolley freight line over the Union Electric Company's Keokuk dam.

Keokuk lost its street railway in 1928, but the railroad tracks and the dam's mile-long electric trolley freight line survive. The dam line's equipment includes a home-built electric flat car and an unmotored heavy-duty crane. The dam's turbines generated power for St. Louis (and the St. Louis streetcar system) over two hundred miles to the south, as they have from the time of the dam's completion in 1913. St. Louis ran its last streetcar in 1966, but powered test runs on its MetroLink light rail line began in July 1992 (the line opened in July 1993) and MetroLink gets power from the dam (via the grid) at certain times.

The dam celebrated its 75th anniversary in 1988. As part of the celebrations, two of Gomaco's replica open cars were trucked in from Ida Grove IA for the party. Car 1976 operated the dam line to Hamilton as the first leg of a circular shuttle which began with visitors walking from Victory Park to the Keokuk Locks, across the locks and into the dam powerhouse. Car 1977 (with its own built-in generator) shuttled passengers back to Victory Park across the Keokuk-Hamilton Bridge, a bus bridging the gap between the end of the wires and Hamilton Junction. Car 1977 also ran a couple of excursions along the railroad (by now known as the Keokuk Junction Railway) east to La Harpe IL.

In 1991 the Keokuk Junction Railway bought four "Strafford" cars from Philadelphia SEPTA's Norristown line, and four Boston PCC cars, of which two were subsequently resold to the Midwest Electric at Mt. Pleasant IA. The cars were to be refurbished and then used on a tourist trolley service to be run from Keokuk to Nowhere IL (about four miles east of Hamilton) in conjunction with the arrival of riverboat gambling in Keokuk.

From June to November 1991, car 161 was leased to Union Electric to transport personnel engaged in converting some of the 25-cycle generators to 60-cycle. With limited parking space on the Keokuk side, workers arriving for the shift parked in Hamilton and then rode the trolley over the dam into the powerhouse. A similar service was operated during the Mississippi River floods of 1993 when for several days, not a single highway or railroad bridge was open in the nearly 300 miles between Muscatine IA and St. Louis MO. Initially, Union Electric allowed pedestrians to walk across the dam, but lack of a sidewalk and safety fences soon led them to organize trolley services instead. For ten days in July 1993, car 161 ran 24 hours a day, carrying nearly 39,000 passengers.

The gambling boats soon left Keokuk for richer pickings, but plans for a tourist trolley went ahead and by 1994, regularly-scheduled electric car service was being offered over the trans-Mississippi company's parent Keokuk Junction Railway. Since the line was unwired, power was supplied by a diesel generator (on a PCC car truck) towed behind the car. Services were occasionally extended from Nowhere to La Harpe as planned, but overall ridership was insufficient to pay even the bridge tolls and the service quit early in 1995. The Keokuk Junction Railway was sold early in 1996. Union Electric's dam trolley line still functions.

CAR	BUILDER AND DATE	TRUCKS	CAR TYPE
Philadelphia SEPTA (P&W) 161/3/5/8	Brill, 1927	Brill 27-MCB-2X	DE DT Suburban
Boston MBTA 3235, 3269	Pullman-Standard, 1945	Clark B-2	SE DT MU PCC

MARYLAND

Frederick

Frederick Trolley Committee, Private collection, not open to the public.

Established in 1988 as the East Street Trolley to provide heritage trolleys along four miles of state-owned rail trackage from East Patrick Street to a planned development at Wormans Mills, it was hoped to have the developer help pay for the project. The group owned Frederick city car body 62, plus the body of Hagerstown and Frederick 171 and SEPTA PCC 2103.

OREGON

Glenwood

The Trolley Park (Oregon Electric Railway Historical Association).

Founded in 1957 to preserve something of the Portland (OR) street railway system, the OERHS moved to Glenwood (40 miles west of Portland) in 1959. The site was once the home of a steam logging railroad and most of the wood-built stabling facilities survived. Streetcars began running in 1963, but the site's remoteness was always problematic. With an unassuming entrance on U.S. 26, halfway between Portland and the Pacific coast, thousands of family travelers whizzed by every summer weekend without the least notion it was there. In the unlikely event it was spotted from an speeding auto, it was usually as a receding speck in the rear-view mirror on a two-lane highway deep in the piney woods with no convenient spot to make a U-turn in safety.

This small museum had to add other attractions to survive; in recent times camping and picnic groves were featured while an interpretive display on the street railway era was a permanent exhibit at the station. The lease on Glenwood expires in 1999 and in 1994 it was announced the OERHS was to join forces with the Antique Powerland Museum at Brooks, OR, south of Portland on I-5 between Wilsonville and Salem. Glenwood operations were to have continued until 1999. However, massive winter storm damage led to a March 13, 1996 decision not to re-open, the last run for the public having been made at the end of the season on October 27, 1995. The first few hundred yards of track were laid at Brooks by November 1995 and a car house will be erected in 1996. The north side of the Glenwood trolley loop was dismantled at the end of 1995 to provide materials for the Brooks line. The OERHS museum fleet will remain at Glenwood only until arrangements are made to transfer them to Brooks.

In 1987, the OERHS demonstrated the feasibility of running trolleys on Portland's Lake Oswego line (Willamette Shore trolley) and recently signed a contract to operate the line for the next few years. Cars for the line are drawn from its Glenwood pool and for further information, please refer back to the Portland OR. entry. (* = 3'6" gauge)

A. City and Suburban Cars

CARS	BUILDER AND DATE	TRUCK	CAR TYPE
Blackpool (England) 48	Home-built, 1926	Blackpool/Hurst Nelson "Preston"	DE DT Double deck city
(This car tows a natural gas-fueled generator for use on the Lake Oswego line.)			
Portland Traction Co. 503	Brill, 1902	Melbourne Type 1	DE DT Semi-convertible
*Portland Traction Co. 506	Brill, 1902	Brill 27-G	DE DT Semi-convertible
(This car is owned by the City of Portland.)			
Portland Traction 813	Brill, 1932	Brill 77-E	DE DT Master Unit
(Later Portland 4012.)			
San Francisco MUNI 1118/59 St. Louis, 1946		Clark B-2	SE DT PCC
(Originally St. Louis PS 1720/27.)			
Sydney (Australia) NSW Govt. Twys. 1187	circa 1913 Meadowbank	Sydney 4	DE DT Type O open/closed

Oporto CCFP 123/38 (Brill, 1909/1910) and 154 III (174 until 1985) (home-built, 1932) belong to Gales Creek Enterprises and remain unsold at GCE's former Glenwood site next to the OERHS Trolley Park. Oporto 160 was sold by GCE in the late 1980s to an unknown buyer in Washington State. San Antonio 300 (American, 1913) and Blackpool, England 731 (home-built, 1959, Blackpool/Hurst Nelson "Preston" Mcguire trucks, SE DT illuminated car "Blackpool Belle," built on open car 163 of 1927) are owned by GCE but remain at Glenwood. They were used on the Lake Oswego line until the end of GCE's operating contract in 1994. OERHS-owned Blackpool 48 was transferred by rail under its own power to Lake Oswego in summer 1995. Portland 813 joined it in 1997. The bodies of Tacoma (WA) Ry. & Power Birney 326 (American, 1917) and Fresno Birneys 62/64 (American, 1919), 74 (St. Louis, 1920) are stored at the park. They are owned by car restorer Tom Mendenhall of 9521 232nd Street SW, Edmonds WA 98020.

B. Interurban Cars

Portland Ry. Lt. & Pwr. 1067	Home-built, 1908	DE DT Interurban coach (body only)	
British Columbia	Home-built, 1946	Unknown	DE DT Interurban coach
El. Rlwy 1304			
(This car is on loan from the Seashore Trolley Museum and was transferred to the Brooks site in 1996.)			

C. Work Cars and Locomotives

Glenwood Elec. Ry. 251, 25	GE, Unknown date	Unknown	DE DT 25 ton Steeple cab locomotives
(Originally Missoula MT E251, E254.)			
Missoula (Montana)	GE, 1903	Unknown	DE DT 35 ton Steeple cab locomotive
Street Ry. 351			
(Later Anaconda Copper Company 351.)			
Glenwood Electric RY. L401	GE, Unknown date	Unknown	DE ST 40 ton Steeple cab locomotive
Portland Traction 1455	McGuire, 1895	Mcguire	DE ST Snow sweeper
(Originally East Side Railways (Portland, OR) 102.)			

D. Electric Trolley Buses

Seattle Metro 604	(Originally 922, then 653)	Twin Coach 40GWFT, 1940

PENNSYLVANIA

Philadelphia

Penn's Landing Trolley, Standard-gauge tourist trolley operated by the Buckingham Valley Trolley Association, PO Box 7285, Philadelphia, PA 19101. (215) 639-2950.

With roots in abortive museum projects at Tansboro NJ and Jobstown NJ, the BVTA began operating the first of its significant collection of historic Philadelphia cars on standard-gauge tracks at New Hope PA in 1975, next to the New Hope and Ivyland RR in Bucks County. A move was made to Penn's Landing in the early 1980s, the cars being housed in covered warehouse piers. The first ran in 1982 over former railroad switching tracks on Delaware Avenue. Through no fault of its own, several moves from pier to pier were forced upon the BVTA and in 1989 it was on the verge of closing down the Penn's Landing servive due to insecurity of tenure. Operation did continue, though several non-operating cars were transferred to open storage at leased property at Front and Laurel in the city. Unhappily, several of these were vandalized early in 1995.

The line was again on the verge of closing in mid-October 1995 when its insurance expired. The increased premiums demanded and the earlier vandalism was too much to bear but the crisis was weathered when financial help was made available at the 11th hour to allow the line to run for another year and the season ended normally on December 17, 1995. Plans for a northerly extension to Spring Garden, plus improvements to the existing line using $1.25 million in ISTEA funds fell apart in the last days of 1995 when PennDOT suddenly insisted that a third party (either the city of Philadelphia or SEPTA) guarantee continued operation and maintenance of the line and extension if BVTA should fail or cease for any reason. Neither party had funding to make such a guarantee and so PennDOT refused to be involved with the trolley line work (part of a related project to improve Delaware Avenue, now renamed Columbus Boulevard). Nor would the city proceed with the line's extension. PennDOT then removed all existing sidings, including Pier 9, BVTA's current carhouse, so cutting off all rail access to the trolley line along Columbus Boulevard.

That was it. The BVTA trustees announced the end of Penn's Landing operations early in January 1996 and began transferring cars elsewhere. By spring 1996, all wire and poles had been removed from Columbus Boulevard and the operating fleet (plus vandalized cars worth salvaging) went to SEPTA's Germantown carhouse. Unhappily on May 31, 1996, in the middle of this move, the Front and Laurel site was again attacked by vandals and several cars were torched. "Hog Island" car (Philadelphia Suburban Red Arrow 26) was severely damaged. Two other Red Arrow cars (including 75) and Philadelphia (PRT) 5205 were also burned.

While the Penn's Landing operation has ceased, the BVTA has not. Its core collection is largely

91

intact and its claim to be the only museum to specialize in Philadelphia/Tristate area cars remains valid. But the vandalism, plus the restricted space available at Germantown, has compelled the BVTA to reassess its present collection based on four criteria: a.) Whether the car had a singular historic impact on the Philadelphia region, b.) Whether duplicates exist elsewhere, c.) Whether needed repairs can be done, d.) Whether spare parts are available. On this basis, BVTA will sell Broad Street subway car 182, subway paint car T-14, Red Arrow (Philadelphia & Western) Bullet 202 and work car 400, SEPTA PCC car 2255 and work motor W-55. This roster is incomplete.

A. City and Suburban Cars

CAR	BUILDER AND DATE	TRUCK	CAR TYPE
Philadelphia SEPTA (Red Arrow) 9	Brill, 1941	Brill 89-ER-1	DE DT Suburban MU "Brilliner"
Philadelphia SEPTA (Red Arrow) 15/17	St. Louis, 1949	St. Louis	DE DT Suburban MU PCC
Wildwood (NJ) Five Mile Beach El. Ry. 24	Brill, 1908	–	DE DT 13-bench open
(Originally New York TARS car. Brill 22E trucks and other Lisbon equipment are available for its restoration.)			
Philadelphia Suburban (Red Arrow) 26	Brill, 1918	Standard C-50	DE DT "Hog Island" city
(Originally Philadelphia PRT/PTC "Hog Island" car 4024.)			
Philadelphia Suburban (Red Arrow) 75/76	Brill, 1926	Brill 27-MCB-3X	DE DT Center-entrance suburban
Philadelphia SEPTA (Red Arrow) 80	Brill, 1932	Brill 89-E-1	DE DT Lightweight suburban
Wilmington (DE) 120	Laclede, 1902	Brill 21-E	ST DE City
Philadelphia SEPTA (P&W) 202	Brill, 1931	Brill 89-E-2	DE DT "Bullet" suburban
Philadelphia SEPTA 2255	St. Louis, 1946	Clark B-2	SE DT PCC
(Originally Kansas City PS 753.)			
Philadelphia SEPTA 2647	St. Louis, 1942	Clark B-2	SE DT PCC
Philadelphia PTC 5205/5327	Brill, 1923	Brill 39-E-2	DE DT City
(5327 is still at Jobstown NJ).			
Philadelphia PRT 8042, 8534	Brill, 1923	Brill 39-E-2	SE DT "Peter Witt" city
(8042 and 8534 are on loan to SEPTA.)			

SEPTA PCC 2701 was scrapped in 1996. SEPTA PCCs 2257/89/2636/53/63, are not part of the BVTA collection, but were stored with BVTA cars at various locations. 2257 (in poor condition) remains at Jobstown NJ. 2289 is with a private owner in Geigertown PA.

B. Interurban Cars

Philadelphia & Western 46	St. Louis, 1907	St. Louis 60-1	DE DT Interurban coach

C. Rapid Transit Cars

Philadelphia SEPTA (Broad St.) 182	Pressed Steel, 1938	Commonwealth	DE DT Subway

D. Work Cars and Locomotives

Hershey (PA) Transit 3	Brill, 1903	Brill 27-MCB	DE DT Construction
(Originally Hummelstown & Campbellstown [PA] Combine 3.)			
Philadelphia SEPTA D-7	Home-built, 1908	Peckham	DE DT Coal Hopper
(Originally PRT steel coal car 2624. Became vacuum cleaner car for subway-surface lines in 1955.)			
McAndrews and Forbes Co. 10	GE, 1925	GE	DE ST 250-volt locomotive
Philadelphia SEPTA T-14	Differential	Curtis D-2	DE DT Subway paint car
(Originally Reading [PA] Differential Dump car 620. Sold to Philadelphia in 1947, became paint car in 1962.)			
Philadelphia SEPTA D-37	Home-built, 1922	Brill 50-E-1	DE DT Line car
Philadelphia SEPTA W-54/55	Brill, 1923	Brill 50-E-1	DE DT Work motor with hoist
Philadelphia SEPTA C-128/143	Brill, 1923	Brill 50-E-2	DE DT Snow sweeper
(C-143 originally snow plow E-204 until rebuilt as snow sweeper in 1927.)			
Philadelphia SEPTA (P&W) 400	Differential	Arch bar	DE DT Side dump
(Originally a Cincinnati & Lake Erie car.)			
Philadelphia SEPTA (P&W) 401	St. Louis, 1907	St. Louis 60-1	DE DT Line car

The station building and visitors' center of the National Capital Trolley Museum is the backdrop for Washington D.C. pre-PCC car 1053 on October 31, 1992.

Halton County Radial Railway's replica Toronto open car 327 is popular with museum visitors, even on chilly fall days, as this October 12, 1975 picture demonstrates.

Two Seashore Trolley Museum members recreate the rear vestibule of Minneapolis 1267 on July 26, 1988.

The Richfol shelter of the Pennsylvania Trolley Museum in October 1991 with Philadelphia Red Arrow Lines car 66.

Laflin Station of the Western Railway Museum in April 1990 as Key System articulated "Bridge" car 182 awaits departure time.

Two Connecticut Company cars at the Connecticut Trolley Museum in August 1979.

Memphis Main Street Trolley 204 southbound at the northern entrance to Main Street Mall.

Dallas 186 heading downtown along McKinney Avenue in May 1991. The tracks were originally laid in 1926, blacktopped in 1956, uncovered and returned to service in 1989.

96

ABBREVIATIONS AND GLOSSARY

Articulated Articulated cars feature two bodies sharing a common truck. Unusual in traditional North American practice, it is common on contemporary light rail cars.

B&QT Brooklyn and Queens Transit Corporation.

BCER British Columbia Electric Railway (Vancouver).

BMT Brooklyn-Manhattan Transit.

BT Baltimore Traction Company.

BTC Baltimore Transit Company.

Birney "safety" car Developed by J. M. Bosenbury, superintendent of motive power and equipment for the Illinois Traction Company and perfected by Charles O. Birney, master mechanic for the Stone & Webster Corporation's portfolio of widely-scattered medium and small-town trolley systems, this was a lightweight one-man operated steel-bodied car with safety features including a controller interlocked with the brakes, car doors and sanding mechanism (dry sand deposited on wet or greasy rails assisted in giving car wheels a good grip and preventing skids). The car could not move before the doors were closed. A "dead-man" feature on the controller instantly applied the brakes if the motorman was incapacitated.

This was the first mass-produced standard streetcar (albeit with minor variations) for universal use and it was simultaneously produced by several manufacturers who built several thousand Birney cars between 1915 and 1926. The car was used to slash out-of-control operating costs and to counter competition from private (automobile) transit. Most Birneys were austerely-finished poor-riding single-truck cars of limited comfort, clearly inferior to the heavy double-truck four-motor cars they replaced. A double-truck Birney was soon developed which eliminated some of the smaller car's vices. There was even a Birney bus, though few were sold.

Boston ER Boston Elevated Railway Company.

Box motor A closed interurban car without windows, used to carry freight. See also express car.

Brilliner An commercially unsuccessful rival to the PCC car produced by the J. G. Brill Company of Philadelphia between 1938 and 1941. *See also PCC.*

CPR City Passenger Railway, Baltimore.

CSL Chicago Surface Lines.

CTA Chicago Transit Authority. Succeeded Chicago Surface Lines in 1947.

CTC City Transit Company, Dayton. Succeeded by Miami Valley RTA in 1971.

CTS Cleveland Transit System. Municipal successor to Cleveland Railway in 1942.

Cable grip A car fitted with a gripping mechanism to latch onto (and off) the cable which provided forward motion. *See also conduit 2.*

California A car for all-year service with a closed compartment in the center and open ends. Developed and most commonly used in California. *See also Convertible, Semi-Convertible.*

Center-entrance A car with entrance and exit in the center of the body. *See also Drop-center.*

City A car built for intensive high-capacity city operation. *See also Birney "safety," Peter Witt, PCC.*

Coach *See Interurban.*

Combine A closed interurban car with one or more compartments for passengers and a separate compartment for mail, baggage or express.

Commuter A heavy self-propelled electric car (or matching trailer) used in short-distance service on railroad lines that except for ownership were "super" interurbans or rapid transit lines.

Conduit

1. Tubing in or under a car body through which the wires for its electrical circuits are drawn.

2. A system of current distribution in which positive and negative conductors carrying the propulsion current are mounted in a channel or tube below street level and accessed by a plow mounted on the car, projecting down into the conduit through a continuous slot in the pavement between the rails. The conduit was a beefed-up modification of that commonly used for cable cars in the 1890s.

The cost of installing a conduit system was about double that of the conventional overhead wire/rail return commonly used. Conduit collection was thus only used in cities where objections to overhead wire could not be overcome. The only permanent installations in North America were in Washington DC and New York's Manhattan Island. It was also found in London (UK), Paris (France) and a handful of other European capital cities. It worked well enough once the bugs were ironed out— London, New York and Washington had over a half-century of intensive operation, using it to the end (1952, 1946 and 1962 respectively). San Francisco's cable cars still pick up their cable via grips protruding from the car floor into a conduit between the rails; the conduit was last renewed in the 1982-1984 period.

Convertible A car that could operate with its sides completely enclosed by panels and window sashes, or with sashes and panels removed (or stored in on-board pockets), so leaving the car completely open. *See also California, Semi-convertible*

DART Dallas Area Rapid Transit.

DE Double-ended. A car with controls and motorman's position at each of its platform ends is a double-ended (or double-end) car. *See also single-ended car.*

DSR Department of Street Railways, Detroit. Also Duluth Street Railway.

DT Double-truck. Double-truck cars are mounted on two swivelling four-wheel trucks which carry the car body, motors, much of the braking equipment, springs and bolsters. A double-truck car has four axles (two per truck), each axle with two wheels. Double-truck cars are generally longer, of higher capacity and speed and better riding than single-truck cars. They may only have one motor in each two-axle truck, but double-trucks with a motor to every axle are more usual. *See also Pedestal truck, radial truck, single-truck, truck.*

Drop-center A center-entrance, two-man operated car in which to speed loading and unloading, the floor is dropped several inches below the level of the body floor to eliminate one of the two platform steps normally encountered when entering a city car. The second step is removed to the car interior, between the center-entrance and each compartment. Occasionally, a ramp is substituted for the interior step. Cars of this type were frequently known as sow-belly cars in North America, particularly in Los Angeles. *See also Hobbleskirt.*

ETB Electric trolley bus (also known as trackless trolley and trolley bus).

ETS Edmonton Transit System.

Elevated A rapid transit car or trailer normally used on an elevated rapid transit system of the kind found in Boston, Chicago, New York and Philadelphia.

Express An interurban box motor car with side doors, used to transport small parcels, baggage and light freight.

FRA Federal Railroad Administration.

FTA Federal Transportation Administration (successor to UMTA).

Heritage trolley A new-build stand-alone tourist trolley line, or trolley service on existing light rail trackage running at least one car native to the city or region's former trolley systems. Also used generically when referring to elderly cars with a heritage connection to the area in which they run or are preserved. *See also Vintage Trolley.*

Hobbleskirt A stepless center-entrance car.

ISTEA Intermodal Surface Transportation Efficiency Act, 1991

Interurban car or coach An electric car used in long-distance high-speed passenger service. Until the mid-1920s, these heavy, lengthy cars more closely resembled steam railroad coaches than streetcars. Lightweight interurban cars were less easily distinguished from ordinary street cars; even the characteristic on-board toilet might be missing.

KCPS Kansas City Public Service Company.

LAMTA Los Angeles Metropolitan Transit Authority.

Lightweight Generally a metal-bodied city car built after World War One, with special attention paid to weight reduction. Some suburban and interurban cars were also built to lightweight designs at this time.

M&MTB Melbourne and Metropolitan Tramways Board (Australia).

MBTA Massachusetts Bay Transportation Authority, Boston. (1964-date)

MSR Market Street Railway, San Francisco.

MTA Metropolitan Transit Authority, Boston. (1948-1964)

MU Multiple-Unit. Cars with multiple-unit equipment could operate as complete trains of two, three, four or more cars, using their own on-board motors and equipment, but under the control of the sole motorman in the lead car. Most commonly found on rapid transit and subway trains, it was also fairly common on the "super" interurbans i.e. those upgraded to the highest standards of the 1920s such as Los Angeles's Pacific Electric and the Chicago, North Shore & Milwaukee. In city and suburban streetcar service, multiple-unit cars were most frequently found in the later PCC era. Today's light rail cars are also multiple-unit equipped cars.

MUNI Municipal—as in San Francisco Municipal Railway (MUNI).

Master Unit A late-1920s lightweight car design of distinctive modern appearance, made by the J. G. Brill Company. A similar car, known as the Electromobile, was made by Perley Thomas.

NOPSI New Orleans Public Service Inc.

NRHS National Railroad Historical Society.

NYCTA New York City Transit Authority.

Nearside A front-entrance and exit pay-as-you-pass car, designed to pick up and set down passengers at the near side of a street intersection so the motorman could exercise constant supervision of the process. Introduction of this design to Philadelphia in 1911 was said to have cut passenger accidents by more than 50%. The type heavily influenced future designs such as the lightweight Birney "safety" car and the heavier "Peter Witt" city car.

OTC Ottawa Traction Company.

Observation An uncommon form of open car for tourist sightseeing in which the seats were tiered as if in a theater.

Open A car open to the weather, usually with cross-bench seating with no central aisle, sometimes with regular seating and a central aisle, occasionally without a roof, sometimes with an enclosed (vestibuled) motorman's platform. These cars were for summer use. *See also California, convertible, semi-convertible.*

P&W Philadelphia & Western. Original owner of the Norristown high-speed line, later owned by Philadelphia Suburban Transportation Company (Red Arrow) and now owned by SEPTA.

PAT Port Authority Transit, Pittsburgh.

PCC A streamlined city car built to the designs of the Presidents' Conference Committee. The PCC was set up in 1929 by the transit industry to establish a research and development program to come up with a modern streetcar to counter bus and automobile competition, cut operating costs and improve comfort and speed. The Committee consisted of several dozen street railway operating and manufacturing companies, each company contributing dues to fund the research. The "million-dollar" streetcar took six years to develop; the first (except for some 1934 and 1935 pre-production samples) hit the streets in 1936. Extensive use of rubber in the truck suspension system and wheels made for a exceptionally smooth and silent-running car, as did the adoption of automotive-type drive shafts between motor and axle, eliminating the noisy traditional gear-and-pinion mechanism which gave the characteristic deep-throated growl still heard on older streetcars and subway trains.

The PCC car body was streamlined in a distinctive manner, reminiscent of a 1934 Chrysler "Airflow" with art deco undertones. The use of newly-developed "Cor-ten" steel in an all-welded stressed-skin body, eliminated the need for a bulky underframe and so the car shed weight without sacrificing strength. The interior was light, airy and uncluttered. All wood finish and trim was gone, together with the dark stains and varnishes previously favored. All seats were upholstered and for the first time interior lights were consistently bright enough to read a newspaper by. Performance was light-years ahead of any car before or since, the PCC having the acceleration of a Ford V8 automobile. This was achieved by new control packages that eliminated the few jerky steps of the traditional street railway hand-operated controller notching mechanism, substituting instead semi-automatic operation of an underfloor-mounted control mechanism with as many as 90 plus notches, put into motion by the motorman through automotive-type foot pedals. This gave silky-smooth acceleration and deceleration. All the Birney car's safety features were incorporated, as was the "Peter Witt" car interior layout on those PCC cars built for two-man operation.

The standardised car and its approved variants (such as Chicago's unique three-door extra-long design, plus the post-war update known as the 1945 PCC car), were marketed by the Transit

Research Corporation, who franchised manufacturers in many countries. As a result, after World War Two the type was built all over Europe (with updated body styling) the Soviet bloc alone building close to 12,000 over the next 40 years. North American production ceased in 1952 after just under 5,000 cars were built, although hundreds of PCC-designed rapid transit cars continued to be made well into the 1960s. PCC cars are still in limited North American transit service today, generally of a heritage type. In Europe, however, they remain in the front-line urban service for which they were designed, especially in the former Soviet-bloc countries.

PRT Philadelphia Rapid Transit Company.

PS Public Service Company (as in Kansas City PS or St. Louis PS).

PTC Philadelphia Transportation Company.

Parlor A luxuriously fitted interurban or city car used for charter service, with individual chairs or seats and (frequently) other fittings, such as carpets, a bar, kitchen, refrigerator etc.

Pedestal truck Universally found on horse cars and occasionally on single-truck electric snow sweeper cars, these are the unsophisticated predecessors of the single truck. Pedestal trucks have no separate frame and consist of a pedestal jaw and journal box mounted directly to the car body. The journal box containing the wheel and axle-end could move vertically in the jaw, but not laterally or horizontally, and the unit contained no springing except for small coils or leaf spring clusters in and around the journal box.

Peter Witt Peter Witt, the street railway commissioner of Cleveland OH. in 1915, gave his name to a new type of two-man double-truck steel-bodied streetcar, first seen in that city. The car had a front entrance, center exit and a pay-as-you-pass fare collection system in which the passengers paid a seated conductor as they passed into the car. Other features included longitudinal seating in the front half of the car (to give a larger standing and circulation area) and normal seating in the rear.

These heavy double-truck cars were developed at the same time as the Birney "safety" cars and shared many of the little car's safety features. But the Witts were exclusively for big-city service, of which they were the savior because of their ability to pick up and set down crowds extremely quickly through their separate entrance and exits. Modification of the type to pay-as-you-enter one-man operation brought city car design to its full maturity; almost all urban buses today still use the front-entrance, pay-as-you-enter, center-exit layout, though the longitudinal seats at the front of the Peter Witt car long ago gave way to more normal cross-seating.

RPO Railway Post Office. Most interurbans and many street railways (especially in the first 15 years of this century) had contracts with the postal authorities and provided specially-equipped cars to carry and sort the mail en route.

RR Railroad.

RT Rapid Transit.

RTA Regional Transportation Authority.

RY Railway.

Radial truck A long-wheelbase single truck supporting a high-capacity car body, in which the axles are allowed some end movement that takes them out of a strictly parallel position to assume a radial movement when rounding sharp curves, easing their passage and smoothing the ride. Radial trucks were uncommon in North America but common in Britain, whose operators loved the economy of a two-motor single truck, but needed a high capacity double-deck body.

Rapid Transit Loosely applied at the beginning of the 20th century to any electric rail or urban streetcar system, the term soon was confined to heavy-rail electric elevated and subway systems.

Red Arrow (Lines) Another name for the Philadelphia Suburban Transportation Company's lines to Ardmore, Media, Norristown Sharon Hill and West Chester.

Replica A car built from new to replicate an older, usually extinct, vehicle. Occasionally, parts of the original (if it still exists) are incorporated into the newly-built replica, as in Calgary 14 at Heritage Park, Calgary or San Antonio 300 on loan to the former Gales Creek Enterprises of Glenwood, Oregon. No comprehensive definition of where an original ceases and a replica begins has yet evolved, but it is a fact of life that almost all restorations of originals back to working order have a percentage of replicated parts in them, especially those that began as chicken coops. This leads to technical problems of provenance and authenticity that get lost in the theater that is an operating trolley museum. It is less of a problem in tourist operation, where authenticity isn't a major issue.

SE Single-end. A car with controls and motorman's position at the forward end only. However, many single-end cars were fitted with back-up controls at the rear for convenience in making back-up and switching moves.

SEPTA Southeastern Pennsylvania Passenger Transportation Authority (Philadelphia area).

SLPS Saint Louis Public Service Company.

ST Single truck. A two-axle four-wheel non-swivelling truck on which a short car body is mounted. The body underframe rests directly on the truck springs or the spring-supported top bar of the truck sideframe. This truck was used extensively in the early electric streetcar days, but in North American conditions of cheaply-built tracks and the need for higher-capacity cars, they were quickly phased out in favor of double trucks for better riding, higher capacity and more powerful vehicles. In Europe, however, single-truck cars were prized for lightness of weight and the economy of two-motor operation. Extra capacity was taken care of (except in the UK) by hanging a trailer car or two in back of a single-truck motor car. Longer-wheelbase single trucks were later developed that accomodated higher-capacity bodies, giving acceptable ride qualities on Europe's better-constructed tracks. *See also double trucks, pedestal trucks, radial trucks.*

San Diego ER San Diego Electric Railway.

San Francisco MUNI San Francisco Municipal Railway.

Semi-convertible A closed car with removeable window sashes that can be taken off the car, dropped into wall pockets, or (most commonly) raised into roof pockets. This last type was developed by the J. G. Brill Company around 1900 and became an industry standard, eliminating the need to keep two sets of car bodies, one enclosed for winter and one open for summer. *See also California car, convertible car, open car.*

Sow-belly *See Drop-center.*

Street car (or streetcar) Today used loosely and interchangeably with trolley and to a lesser extent with light rail, the term "street car" was originally used to identify cars used only in city or urban passenger service, as distinguished from cars used in suburban or interurban service.

Suburban A car designed for short runs into suburban or rural areas, with mixed street and private right-of-way running. Suburban cars were slightly larger, heavier and speedier than city cars, but were not designed with the attention to door and interior passenger flow required of cars serving intensively-traveled urban routes.

TARS Third Avenue Railway System, New York City.

TCRT Twin Cities Rapid Transit Company (Minneapolis/St. Paul).

TMER&L The Milwaukee Electric Railway and Light Company.

TTC Toronto Transportation (later Transit) Commission

Trolley (or trolley car) A generic term commonly used for an electric car which gets power from an overhead wire collected by a trolley pole on the car roof. It is used interchangeably with the term street car (or streetcar) in many areas of North America and is also used generically (though inaccurately) when talking of cars getting electricity via a third rail or conduit.

Truck (s) A frame or carriage supported on one or more axles and pairs of wheels. Can be single, double or radial. If a truck has motors, it is a motor truck. If it has no motors, it is a trailer truck. Motor trucks can be single motor or double motor.

UMTA Urban Mass Transit Administration (predecessor of the present FTA).

UR&E United Railway & Electric Company, Baltimore.

UR United Railways of St. Louis.

URR United Railroads of San Francisco.

Vestibule An enclosed car platform which protected the motorman from the weather. Cars so fitted were said to be vestibuled. Confusingly, open cars could be vestibuled, while closed cars could be unvestibuled. Indeed, early electric closed cars (like their horse car predecessors) were always unvestibuled. Although the term isn't used today, light rail cars are all vestibuled cars.

Vintage trolley A new-build stand-alone tourist trolley line, or trolley service on existing light rail trackage using old cars not native to the city or region's former trolley systems. Also used generically when referring to elderly cars that have no heritage connection to the area in which they run or are preserved. See also heritage trolley

Former Melbourne car 518 northbound on Seattle's Alaskan Way, September 6, 1989.

All stations on Seattle's Waterfront trolley are handicapped-accessible as can be seen in this view of Broad Street Station in August 1991.

PRINCIPAL CAR, CAR TRUCK, BUS AND ELECTRIC TROLLEY BUS MANUFACTURERS

ACF American Car and Foundry Company (later ACF Industries) New York, St. Charles, MO. 1899-date. Primarily a railroad passenger and freight car builder, the company is still in business. Streetcar and interurban manufacture was done on a limited scale between 1905 and 1931. Rapid transit and subway cars were built until the late 1960s.

ACF/Brill Philadelphia, PA. 1926-1953. A joint venture between ACF and J. G. Brill allowing the latter to design buses powered with the ACF-owned Hall-Scott underfloor pancake motor. Between 1926 and 1944 buses were marketed under the ACF name only. 1926-1953.

AEC Associated Equipment Company, Southall, Middlesex, England. 1912-1962. Acquired by Leyland Motors (later British Leyland), 1962, last AEC buses built 1968. Known as the builder of London's buses (the still-operating Routemaster was an AEC design), AEC built ETBs under its own name until 1942, and as a part of the British United Traction consortium until the 1960s.

ALCO American Locomotive Company, New York. Manufactured electric railway trucks from circa 1903, railroad trucks exclusively from about 1912.

ALCO/GE Joint electric locomotive building enterprise between the American Locomotive Company and General Electric.

AM General AM General, South Bend, IN. Manufactured Flyer bus and electric trolley bus designs in the US from 1974-1979.

American American Car Company, St. Louis MO. 1891-1931. Acquired by Brill Company in 1902.

ASEA Allmanna Svenska Elektriska Aktiebolaget, Vasteras, Sweden. circa 1906-date.

Baldwin Baldwin Locomotive Works, Philadelphia PA.

Baldwin/Westinghouse Joint electric locomotive building enterprise between the Baldwin Locomotive Works and Westinghouse Electric and Manufacturing Company.

Barney & Smith Barney & Smith Car Company, Dayton OH. 1849-1923.

Bemis Bemis Car Box Company, Springfield MA. Manufactured street railway trucks circa 1890-circa 1905.

Blackwell Canadian truck designs, built by the Montreal Steel Company circa 1900-1914.

Briggs Briggs Carriage Company, Amesbury, MA. 1890-1903.

Brill J. G. Brill & Company, Philadelphia PA. 1868-1954. Last streetcar was built in 1941, but transit vehicle production, including buses, electric trolley buses and (under license) streetcar trucks continued until 1954. Known as Brill Corporation after a merger with ACF in 1925.

Brownell Brownell Car Company (earlier known as Brownell & White Car Company) St. Louis, MO. 1875-1900. Acquired by American Car Company in 1900.

Brush Brush Electrical Engineering Company, Loughborough England. 1889-date. Primarily a railroad manufacturer (including steam diesel and electric locomotives), streetcar bodies were built from 1890-1937, electrical equipment and trucks from about 1900. Bus bodies were built until 1951.

CCF Canadian Car & Foundry Company, Montreal, PQ. 1909-1966. Acquired 1966 by Hawker-Siddeley Canada and became their Canadian Car Division in 1966, moving to Thunder Bay ON. Later acquired by Bombardier.

CCF/Brill A marketing arrangement between CCF and Brill allowing the latter's buses and electric trolley buses to be built by CCF in Canada under licence. See also St. Louis/CCF.

CCFL Companhia Carris de Ferro de Lisboa, Portugal. 1888-date. The streetcar operator of Lisbon, Portugal, which made hundreds of its own cars.

CCFP Companhia Carris de Ferro do Porto, Portugal. 1893-1946. The streetcar operator of Oporto, Portugal, which made many of its own cars. Since municipalization in 1946, known as Servico de Transportes Colectivos do Porto (STCP).

Carter Carter Brothers, Newark CA. 1886-circa 1897.

Cincinnati Cincinnati Car Company, Cincinnati, OH. 1902-1931. Built streetcars, interurbans and rapid transit cars.

Clark Clark Equipment Company, Battle Creek MI. circa 1928-date. Built PCC car trucks.

Commonwealth Commonwealth Steel Company, Granite City, IL. Circa 1919-1930. Merged with General Steel in 1930, but Commonwealth railroad trucks continued to be made for years afterwards.

Cummings *See McGuire-Cummings.*

Curtis Curtis Truck Company, Decatur IL. Operated circa 1905-1910. Several of E. A. Curtis's truck designs were also built by other manufacturers.

Danville Danville Car Company, Danville, IL. 1900-1913. Acquired by J. G. Brill in 1908.

EMB Electro-Mechanical Brake Company, West Bromwich, England. 1908-date. Built trucks, brake-systems and streetcar spare parts.

English Electric English Electric Company Ltd., Preston, England. A 1918 merger of several early railroad and streetcar manufacturers, its last streetcars and trucks were built in the 1930s. The company was merged into a larger conglomerate, which is still in business. An airplane manufacturing venture was successful and eventually became a component of the present British Aerospace.

Fiegel Fiegel Company, Brooklyn NY. 1873-1894.

Flxible Flxible Inc., Loudonville, OH. 1919-1996. Acquired Twin Coach 1953.

Flyer Flyer Industries Ltd., Winnipeg, Manitoba. 1930-date. Now known as New Flyer.

Ford Ford Motor Company, Detroit. Built small buses from the 1930s to the 1950s.

GE General Electric, Erie, PA. 1892-date.

GM General Motors, Detroit MI. 1908-date. Built buses (as Yellow Coach) 1925-1943, as GM 1944-1987.

Gebruder Schoendorff *See Siemens-Duewag.*

General Steel General Steel, later General Steel Castings, Granite City, IL. Acquired Commonwealth Steel in 1930 and continued to sell Commonwealth trucks for decades, plus truck designs of their own, almost all for railroad or subway cars. Acquired St. Louis Car Company in 1960. Still in business.

Gilbert and Bush One of several partnerships based in Troy NY, involving Uri Gilbert or his son, and others. Gilbert first surfaced circa 1820; the firm's final incarnation being the Gilbert Car Manufacturing Company, 1882-1895. The Gilbert & Bush Company period, together with the earlier Gilbert, Bush and Company lasted from 1864 to 1882.

Gloucester Gloucester Carriage & Wagon Company, Gloucester, England. A railroad car manufacturer, it built rapid transit and subway cars until the 1960s.

Gomaco Gomaco, Ida Grove, IA. 1982-date. A major manufacturer of road-paving machines, Gomaco has since 1982 built many replica streetcar bodies for heritage use. Chicago, Melbourne and Philadelphia cars and parts have been used to make them operable. Additionally, Gomaco has restored several existing museum cars and Melbourne W2 cars to operating condition.

Hall-Scott Hall Scott Motor Car Company, Berkeley, CA. 1907-1926. Acquired by ACF Industries in the early 1920s. ACF's Hall-Scott Division closed circa 1954.

Hammond J. S. Hammond & Company, San Francisco, CA. 1883-1907.

Hicks Hicks Car and Locomotive Works, Chicago, IL. circa 1891-circa 1910.

Holman Holman Car Company, San Francisco, CA. 1883-1913.

Home-built Many car maintenance and repair facilities were huge operations and in cities such as Milwaukee, Minneapolis/St. Paul, New York and St. Louis, these facilities were quite capable of designing and building their own cars, trucks and equipment -and did.

Hurst Nelson and Company Motherwell, Scotland. 1893-1958. Primarily a railroad builder with a large export market, rapid transit cars, street car bodies and trucks were built until 1934, although spare parts continued to be made until 1952.

Jackson & Sharp Jackson & Sharp Company, Wilmington DE. Circa 1865-1901. Acquired by American Car & Foundry (ACF) in 1901 and continued producing cars under the ACF name.

James Moore Melbourne, Australia.

Jewett Jewett Car Company, Newark, OH. 1894-1918. Best known as an interurban car builder.

Jones Jones' Sons Car Company, Watervliet NY 1839-1922. Streetcars made between 1864 and 1912.

Kuhlman G. C. Kuhlman Car Company, Cleveland, OH. 1892-1932. Acquired by J. G. Brill in 1904.

Laclede Laclede Car Company, St. Louis, MO. 1883-1905. Acquired by St. Louis Car Company in 1903.

Laconia Laconia Car Company, Laconia, NH. 1881-1928.

Leyland Leyland Motors Ltd., (later British Leyland) Leyland, Lancashire, England. Bus manufacturer. 1905-1992.

Mack Mack Bus and Coach, Allentown, PA.

Marmon-Herrington Marmon-Herrington Co. Indianapolis, IN 1946-1959

McGuire McGuire Manufacturing Company, Chicago, IL. 1888-circa 1905, then became known as McGuire-Cummings Manufacturing Company and soon moved to Paris IL., later known as the Cummings Car & Coach Company. Last streetcar built circa 1930, company out of business by 1943.

M&MTB Melbourne and Metropolitan Tramways Board, Victoria, Australia. 1919-1983.

National National Steel Car Corporation, Hamilton, ON. 1913-date.

Newburyport Newburyport Car Manufacturing Company, Newburyport, MA. 1887-1905.

Niles Niles Car and Manufacturing Company, Niles OH. 1901-1917. Primarily an interurban car builder.

Osgood-Bradley Osgood-Bradley Car Company, Worcester, MA. Circa 1833-1930 under slightly different names, of which this was the final version after acquisition in 1910 by Standard Steel. Standard Steel was acquired in 1934 by Pullman and the new company was known as Pullman-Standard. All Pullman electric trolley buses and Pullman-Standard PCC cars were built in the former Osgood-Bradley plant until 1951.

Ottawa Ottawa Car Manufacturing Company, Ottawa, ON. 1891-1947.

Patterson & Corbin Patterson and Corbin, St. Catherines, ON. 1888-circa 1896.

Peckham Peckham Street Car Wheel and Axle Co. Kingston, NY. Also known at various times as Peckham Motor Truck and Wheel Company, Peckham Truck Company, Peckham Manufacturing Company and New York Car and Truck Company. Circa 1890-1906. Peckham then moved to Britain permanently and began to specialize in radial single-truck designs, which were produced under his name by the Brush Company until the 1940s.

Perley Thomas Perley A. Thomas Car Works, High Point NC. 1917-date. Now known as Thomas Built Buses.

Pressed Steel Pressed Steel Car Company, Pittsburgh, PA. 1896-1954. Did not build streetcars until 1906.

Preston Preston Car and Coach Company, Preston ON. 1908-1921.

Pullman Pullman Company, (earlier Pullman Palace Car Company) Pullman (Chicago) IL. 1867-1934. Railroad equipment manufacturer, which also built streetcars.

Pullman-Standard Pullman-Standard Car Manufacturing Company, Pullman (Chicago) IL. 1929-1980 (?). All references to Pullman-built PCCs mean Pullman-Standard. The last streetcar was built in 1951 as was the last electric trolley bus for the domestic market; electric trolley bus orders for South American customers were built for a few more years. Pullman-Standard also built rapid transit and subway cars, the last being delivered to New York in the late 1970s.

Russell Russell Car & Foundry Company, sometimes known as Russell Car and Snow Plow Company.

STCP Servicio de Transportes Colectives do Porto (Portugal). 1946-date. Present name of Oporto's urban mass transit operator.

St. Louis St. Louis Car Company, St. Louis MO. 1887-1974. Last electric trolley coach built 1951, last streetcar built 1952, railroad passenger, commuter and freight cars, rapid transit and subway cars built until closure in 1974.

St. Louis/CCF A marketing arrangement whereby St. Louis Car built body shells and supplied trucks for PCC cars and CCF finished the cars off in their Canadian plant for sale to Canadian customers.

Siemens-Duewag German car builder of Dusseldorf, with a light rail assembly plant in Sacramento, CA. Siemens began in the 1870s and remains a premier electrical manufacturer. Duewag began in Dusseldorf in the 1880s as the furniture and shopfitting manufacturers Gebruder Schoendorff, who turned to street railway car manufacture just after World War One. Deprived of their business by Nazi anti-Jewish laws in 1933, the Schoendorff operation was turned over by the Nazis to a creditor bank, who in 1935 sold the going concern to interests who manufactured under the Duwag (later Duewag) name. The merger with Siemens came about during the 1970s.

Standard Standard Steel Car Company, Butler PA. 1904-1906, Standard Motor Truck Company, Newcastle PA. 1906-1929.

Stephenson John Stephenson Car Company New York NY 1831 until circa 1900, then Elizabeth NJ. Acquired by J. G. Brill Company in 1904, closed 1917.

Stone & Webster Stone & Webster Corporation, Boston MA. 1889-date. The Stone & Webster Corporation held a portfolio of public utilities in the first quarter of the 20th century that included more than a score of widely-scattered medium and small-town trolley systems. They built no cars themselves, but from 1912 developed a uniform city car design for their properties which was also frequently specified by non-Stone & Webster properties for their systems. Stone and Webster's Charles O. Birney was responsible for developing the single-truck lightweight "safety" car that bears his name, for use on their properties. Again, non-Stone & Webster properties quickly latched on to this type.

TCRT Twin Cities Rapid Transit (Minneapolis/St. Paul) built its own cars from 1908 to the late 1920s.

Taunton Taunton Locomotive Manufacturing Co. Taunton, MA. Circa 1847-circa 1923.

Taylor circa 1900-circa 1925

Twin Coach Twin Coach Company; Kent OH. 1927-1955. Acquired by Flxible Co., Loudonville OH, 1955.

UCC Union Construction Company, Feltham, England. 1929-1933. Existed on paper from 1905 to 1929, taken over by London Transport in 1933.

UEC United Electric Car Company, Preston, England. 1905-1918. Predecessor component of English Electric Company.

Umbachi/Sharyo Japanese manufacturing syndicate.

United Railways United Railways of St. Louis. 1899-1927. Built its own cars and trucks between 1903 and 1927.

Wason Wason Manufacturing Company, Springfield MA. 1845-1907, when it was taken over by the J. G. Brill Company. Finally closed 1931.

Western Flyer *See Flyer Industries.*

Westinghouse Westinghouse Electric and Manufacturing Company, Pittsburgh, PA. 1886-date.

White The White Company, Cleveland, OH. 1900-1995. Built buses 1915-1953.

Woeber Woeber Brothers Carriage Company, Denver, CO. circa 1880-1920.

Yellow Coach Yellow Truck and Coach Manufacturing Co. Pontiac, MI. 1923-1943. Wholly owned by General Motors, the Yellow coach name was dropped after 1943 and manufacture of buses resumed in 1944 under the General Motors name.